FRIENDS
OF ACPL

8-26-70

BOOKS *by* ROGER CARAS

ANTARCTICA
Land of Frozen Time

DANGEROUS TO MAN

WINGS OF GOLD

THE CUSTER WOLF

LAST CHANCE ON EARTH

NORTH AMERICAN MAMMALS

SARANG

MONARCH OF DEADMAN BAY

PANTHER!

SOURCE OF THE THUNDER
The Biography of a California Condor

Source of the Thunder

Source of the Thunder

The Biography of a California Condor

by ROGER CARAS

ILLUSTRATIONS BY CHARLES FRACÉ

Foreword by Roland C. Clement

Boston Little, Brown and Company *Toronto*

COPYRIGHT © 1970 BY ROGER A. CARAS

ALL RIGHTS RESERVED. NO PART OF THIS BOOK MAY BE REPRODUCED IN ANY FORM OR BY ANY ELECTRONIC OR MECHANICAL MEANS INCLUDING INFORMATION STORAGE AND RETRIEVAL SYSTEMS WITHOUT PERMISSION IN WRITING FROM THE PUBLISHER, EXCEPT BY A REVIEWER WHO MAY QUOTE BRIEF PASSAGES IN A REVIEW.

LIBRARY OF CONGRESS CATALOG CARD NO. 70–121419

FIRST EDITION

Published simultaneously in Canada
by Little, Brown & Company (Canada) Limited

PRINTED IN THE UNITED STATES OF AMERICA

S 1547015

Just for Pamela . . .

FOREWORD

MORE THAN WE KNOW, we are forced to live by symbols because the total reality of this wonderful, dangerous world we live in is too complex for us.

The California condor, long the Thunder Bird of American Indians, has in our day become a symbol of the pitifully reduced inheritance of wilderness that earlier, profligate generations handed down to us. There is a hint in Mr. Caras's insightful account of a big bird's journey through time-space that our survival may depend, like the condor's, on forces within ourselves we have not yet mastered, nor even grown fully aware of.

This sensitive, necessarily fictionalized but honest reconstruction of a condor's life history, is both delightful reading and a rare excursion behind the mask of our self-conscious pretensions.

Unlike Mr. Caras's condor, we can reflect that Nature may indeed have "many things on her mind," and that it will pay us to slow down in reshaping the only planet we have, treasure our few remnants of wilderness for mind and soul stretching, and insist that the condor be preserved as a symbol of Nature's way. It will then also serve as a monument to the day of our own reawakening to the fact that man and Nature are one.

Roland C. Clement
Vice President
National Audubon Society

Source of the Thunder

Chapter One

SEVERAL BILLION YEARS had passed since the sun's middle-sized child had established an orbit around its parent star. It was one of nine, larger than four, smaller than four, but it was unique within its own family in a number of ways. Its position between sister planets Venus and Mars placed it approximately ninety-three million miles from its sun. That distance assured the infant of a temperature neither too hot nor too cold to permit certain critical chemical reactions to occur. New amalgamations of basic elements would be formed. One day, some of these substances would reproduce themselves; they would live.

The mass of the new planet, and a density greater than that of any other in the family, had provided it with a surface gravity strong enough to hold a thin layer of gas to itself. It would have an atmosphere. That which would live would be sustained.

Lifeless, turbulent, fierce in the extremes of its infancy, the new planet spun around on its own axis once every twenty-four hours while hurtling through space at a speed of eighteen and a half miles a second. The matrix of space being close to a complete vacuum, even these terrific velocities failed to abrade the new child of the solar system. Tightly gripped by the sun's gravitational field it spun, showered with debris of both matter and energy, building its own atmosphere as it went. Gases boiled free from the yet unestablished rocks and the shape and texture of the ball evolved from internal forces and the basic laws governing matter in the cosmos. Cosmic radiation rained down unimpeded and chemical reactions occurred that can barely be contemplated. Although much of what was really important happened on a microscopic level, the larger events must have been horrific in force and violence. The din, unwitnessed though it was, must have been incredible once there were enough molecules in the gaseous envelope to bounce against each other.

And so the first eons passed. One planet out of nine moving around a sun that itself was part of a system of a hundred and fifty billion suns (the system being one of billions upon billions of systems), surging through its elemental times creating its own history. And that history included the most awesome of all miracles, the evolution of raw chemicals into a self-duplicating state called life. That state, once it had come into being, assured the planet of immortality, for mortality and immortality are a continuum, one but an extension of the other.

After the planet had been some three billion years in orbit, a blue-green algae appeared and the complex molecules began their march. Upward from the slime and the reeking chemical baths cradled in rocks still hot from their early history, life spread and diversified. The forms life took became increasingly more complex. Single cells learned how to live together and, in time, strange creatures, some even monstrous, inhabited the planet. Scorpionlike Eurypterids more than eight feet long, brachiopods and trilobites, clams and cystoids, horseshoe crabs, shrimp, snails, and jawless fish spread, changed, spawned new and more successful forms, and vanished. A few resisted time and have lasted on to our present day. Ammonites and nautiloids, lungfish and sharks, labyrinthodonts and forms we do not yet know moved onward. It was a time of experimentation and the diversification was endless.

Competition became more keen and the seas were not enough. In time animals were crawling and walking upon the land. Some forms left only a trail of slime to mark their passage, others footprints. Those that were compelled by their biology to return periodically to the sea gave rise to higher forms that were not, and reptiles, bizarre, enormous, diverse reptiles arisen from amphibians, themselves arisen from fish, ruled the world. Some of these, awesome beyond belief, returned to the sea and prevailed there as their cousins reigned on land, where mountains were yet to be born. It was the time of giants and although the brain complex enough to conjure up nightmare images was still hundreds of millions of years in the future, the nightmarish creatures themselves were a reality. Dragonflies were as big as modern hawks, salamanders so large their bones would one day be confused with those of men.

Once upon the land the reptiles were free to explore and experiment with many ways of life. No avenues were untried and those that elected to remain behind perished for the most part, while those that went on ahead to new ways ended in glory or vanished. Glory, of course, was survival. Five large suborders of reptiles spread out with thousands of species. One of these suborders, the thecodont reptiles known to us now as Pseudosuchia, had an appointment with destiny on two levels. From their midst arose the ponderous dinosaurs who for millions of years would possess the planet and then forever tantalize later creatures who would come to know their bones. Even earlier they had evolved specialized forms that took the thin layers of gas above the earth into their ken. They learned to fly.

The archosaurs, giant reptiles still, solved the problem of flight with staggeringly large batlike wing-membranes as much as twenty-five feet across. Although they flew, they were not birds. Their jaws were heavily armed with the gripping and tearing teeth of the carnivores and only the earliest suggestion of feathers could be detected in their epidermal scales. The hint existed only in that the scales were twice as long as wide with fine striations running out from a central axis. Still, the hint and the promise were there.

The earth, although now stable in its position within the solar system, had not yet found inner peace. Volcanic eruptions tore the surface apart and massive quakes shook whole continents, sending frenzied seas across the land. It is believed by many that entire continents shifted and shunted around the surface of the globe during those terrible times. Cracks and fissures opened, and burning gases spewed forth in geysers that painted the sky. Steam rolled across the land in billowing clouds and the mists of time concealed millions of secrets, any one of which would be critical to our understanding of our world if it could be revealed today. But, too often, what went into the mists dissolved there and today we are far richer in conjecture than in facts. In our souls we can dream of those times, but we do not know them.

One of the most crucial of these secrets may be lost to us forever; more accurately, it was a linked series of happenings. We have no fossil record of the many stages those primitive flying reptiles knew until the relatively recent period of one hundred and fifty million years ago. Then it was that *Archaeopteryx* flew, then, during the Jurassic period. Its flight was not strong and probably carried it for short distances only. It was a light bird, crow-sized, although its bones were not yet hollow. The bones of its tail were still unfused and had twenty free vertebrae to accent its reptilian beginnings. A single feather grew out from each side of these unbirdlike tail vertebrae. There are no links to connect this first known bird with the flying lizards, but from somewhere within the reptilian scheme they had come.

There were many other ways, too, in which *Archaeopteryx* differed from the birds of our time. There was a distinct hand with free-moving and well-clawed fingers, the pelvic bones were unfused, still held together by ligaments after the fashion of the reptile.

The teeth again linked it to its reptilian past. Yet, it was a bird and it flew and it had within it the potential of the eight thousand species of birds we know today. This wonderful creature was without beauty but even in the impressions of its bones we can detect its solemn vow to one day grace the world with color, song, and charm.

Once again the veil of time floated across a world no longer infant but still new and rich in possibilities. The birds that arose from *Archaeopteryx* were lightweight and fragile and left fewer records than heavier-boned creatures on other evolutionary tracks. As we seek its path today, this branch of evolution is far more tantalizing than revealing. It skips in and out of fogbanks, revealing itself only rarely, and then briefly, giving us only the barest hints of the wonders that once were and can never be again, at least on this planet. The fact that we can never know their colors, their songs, or their nests must forever taunt us. What trills and runs did dinosaurs hear each spring as these ancient birds sought their mates? Or were they mute, or did they hiss like snakes?

Change was constant, we know, and hundreds, then thousands, of new bird species evolved. Each had packed within it signs of its reptilian heritage and promises of its avian future. Thirty million more years passed, with the force of evolution surging into every new channel it could discover, and the Cretaceous shales were laid down upon the earth. In that time, the modern bird form was suggested. Gull-like birds flew over land that would one day be known as Kansas, Montana, and Texas. Their brains were small compared to those of birds today but the reptile phase was demonstratably over. Elsewhere, loonlike birds, still equipped with teeth, fed on fish, and birds not unlike our herons, geese, and cormorants found their places. The dinosaurs were already dying off, for their potential had been exhausted and the very qualities that made them awesome proved to be their undoing. In the terrestrial environment their size was a cul-de-sac. In the seas, the mammals had better evolutionary ideas.

Some sixty-five million years ago, when most mammals were still small and harmless, twenty-seven families of modern birds already existed. Grouse, swifts, auks and penguins, sandpipers, bustards, grebes and cuckoos, Evolution had already established these paths and saw in them systems worth developing. She began their refinement.

Within another thirty million years Nature had found the ways of the storks, the plovers, the turkeys, pigeons, parrots, and sparrows to her liking. Ten million more years, the petrels, falcons, and oyster catchers added their survival skills and the Miocene was born. Land areas that no longer exist were populated and sea birds flew over open oceans where island chains were yet to be born. The only thing in which Nature sought permanence was in the force of life itself.

All of this progress was not without its casualties. Nature was quick to discard experiments whose promise was not as great as that of others and the extinction of species was as ready as their evolution. It was in the Pliocene, no more than ten million years ago, that bird species probably reached the maximum. By that time all modern bird genera were in existence, and many we no longer know. Mammals, also descended from reptiles, were evolving as rapidly and the hint of man was already in the loins of ancestral apelike creatures. It may have been that long ago when the first stick was raised up as a club. It may one day be demonstrated that this was the one irremedial mistake Nature ever made. By creating a creature over whose destiny she might one day lose control she may have sacrificed her hold on this one planet, at least.

And so the form of life we know of as birds had come to be. On the gases that seeped up through the rock crevasses of continents still resting on molten beds they flew. They were hatched by the billions, died by the billions, but the power of their flight into time never weakened. It was a successful experiment and from the moment it was launched its outcome was assured. No catastrophe could stop the force of bird life, no competition could do more than sharpen it and force it to improve itself. Time was the honing stone, Evolution the edge-hungry blade. It is only in the last few moments of bird history that any creature has lived capable of the concept of beauty, but that beauty has been here these millions of years. It was Nature's plan then and now, we can believe, that it should always be. There are too few flaws in the design to allow us to think otherwise.

For millions of years the Cretaceous seas had been depositing their sediments in the depression that ran from far north in Canada to deep into Mexico. Between eighty and ninety million years ago, while the dinosaurs and toothed birds still held sway, a revolution began along the line of this enormous trough. The Laramide Revolution, one of the most awesome upheavals in the long and tortured history of the Western Hemisphere, began the thrusting and faulting that would eventually fold a portion of the entire continent upwards until the ragged edges of rocks torn from their bed beneath the sea would reach the sky. The Rocky Mountains were born. From Alaska to the heart of Central America the colossal peaks rose in a range five hundred miles wide in places. Not since pre-Cambrian times, nearly five hundred million years earlier, had such gross physical forces played upon the crust of the earth. In the east, two thousand miles away, the Appalachian Mountains were already a hundred million years old when this new range began its march from below sea level to the sky.

Although erosion began immediately, and some peaks were already beginning their infinitely slow decline before others arose nearby, the great chain of upheaved rock formed then, as now, an enormous barrier. On one side, in the east, the slopes descended to monotonous flat plains. On the other, in the west, they ran down into untidy land that again and again flung great parapets upward until at last the continent came to rest in the sea.

It is likely that active volcanoes throughout the region added their influence to the geological confusion and over a period of millions of years the continent struggled to stabilize itself. Thrust after thrust contributed to the complexity of the revolution until slowly the shape of the land was established, and it rested in relative quiet for the millions of years the forces of heat and cold, wind and water would need to carve the monoliths back down to the level of the sea. That period is still in its infancy.

No one can know how many animals and birds, individuals, species, and perhaps genera were lost in the upheavals. How successful the ancient birds were at escaping the cataclysms we cannot know but through and beyond it all, bird life on either side of the mountains continued to develop. As the mountains came to rest, first in one area and then another, the winged creatures, and then those that crawled and walked, began a reinvasion and the Rocky Mountains, too, had its fauna.

Although the biography of every living creature properly begins when the planet was still an infant, the story of our condor will be reckoned from the wonder-time of North American fauna, the Pleistocene, the final epoch of the seventy-million-year-long Cenozoic era. Seldom has animal life known more fascinating diversity or greater numbers than during this epoch. Men living today who have an interest in such things can but weep for not having seen it. We can know it now only from the mountains of bones we uncover. They taunt us, they tantalize, and we struggle suspended between awe and frustration. What a time it was!

By the time the Pleistocene dawned, the horse, a line of evolution begun in North America seventy million years earlier, had established itself in relatively modern form and had begun its march across the land bridge that existed on the roof of the Pacific Ocean to spread throughout Asia and finally Europe. Although extinct here by the time settlers arrived from Europe, they existed then in herds the size of which we can barely imagine. Stocky, probably uniform in color, heavy-headed and bristle-maned, they grazed their way over enormous plains and scattered in wild confusion at the approach of carnivores.

Giant wolves, whose counterparts exist nowhere on earth today, hunted, probably in family groups and occasionally in larger packs. *Smilodon*, the saber-toothed cat, stalked his victims as a solitary hunter and literally stabbed his prey to death with canines that were flattened and scimitarlike, with finely serrated edges. Biting, in the normal sense of the word, was impossible, for these enormous tusks blocked entrance into the mouth. The cats probably struck much as venomous snakes do today. They ranged from the shores of the Pacific Ocean eastward to Pennsylvania, and existed in surprising numbers.

That such great numbers of these terrifying cats and their canine counterparts, the dire wolves, thrived, is further testimony to the numbers of prey animals that were there to feed them.

The giant ground sloths, short-faced immigrants from Central and South America, spread across the land to fall prey to the marauding bands of wolves and the solitary stealth of the stabbing cats. When on all fours, these sloths stood more than four feet at the shoulder; they have no counterparts surviving into modern times. They were found everywhere, inoffensive browsers with neither speed nor sudden wit at their disposal.

Pronghorns, erroneously called antelopes, similar in most ways to those few that still exist among us, ranged in large herds and frustrated the hunters with their speed and wariness.

Large camels wandered across North America; mastodons, no less elephantlike than the mammoths, existed in vast numbers. Short-faced bears even larger than the existing giants on Kodiak Island, coyotes related to those of today, and many smaller creatures filled each available niche in the ancient ecology. Peccaries, lionlike cats distinct from both the contemporary sabertooths and pumas, tapirs, foxes, and many other forms that would not seem strange to us today were there. Rattlesnakes were by then an old idea and lizards, diminutive reminders of far more ancient times, abounded.

The wonder of the Pleistocene was not limited to animals that wore fur and scales, however, for the birds were as wondrous, and here our story starts.

Chapter Two

THE SUMMER, like the thousands that had preceded it, had been relatively dry. Although the sea was only a few miles away to the west, the sandy flat with the scattered oak, hackberry, and juniper stands was like an internal zone. The low mountains that cupped the area in on three sides were not very impressive but rose just high enough to give the winds sweeping in from the sea a vertical lift that kept the skies over the bowl fairly clear much of the time. On days when the winds were slow or absent, moisture-laden air drifting in casually from the warm seas lingered there and the humidity would rise. But active precipitation was light and scarce.

Although ringed by low hills, the sandy flats were not isolated. Numerous cuts through the hills, many of them nothing more than reminders that rivers, like animals, live and die, provided pathways for wildlife to and from other regions. The rising thermals were particularly beneficial to the soaring birds and they came and went, often at high altitudes.

It was the late Pleistocene, and far to the north and east the third interglacial, a minor one compared to the one that had gone before the now defunct Illinoian glaciation, was coming to a close. Although relatively short in duration it had sent the ice sheets creeping guiltily back toward the Arctic and had seen the temperatures in America's midlands rise sharply. It had guided the northward migration of millions of animals whose ancestral forms had been driven southward thousands of years earlier. This was about to change again, however, as for the fourth time ice sheets were forming and moving toward the south; the Wisconsin glaciation was on the march.

Further to the north, in the flatlands of central Canada, forests were already vanishing, turning to pulp beneath the grinding weight of ice a mile or more deep. Across an enormous front, the ice sheet was edging forward as inexorably as the movement of the planet. The frigid air mass that hovered along the front sucked moisture from the air and deposited it in rime and frozen frost. Snowstorms swept across the sheet, adding to its thickness. At a depth of twenty-eight feet the snow compacted itself into ice. Electric storms crashed along the glacier's face and once again the continent trembled before the fury of an ice age.

To the south and west, though, matters were less urgent. The land was changing there as well, but in a more orderly manner. The higher mountains had their own glaciers but they were small, personal affairs. Snow fell and occasionally a valley would be lost for a few months, simply filled up with snow, and rockslides answered snowslides, but all this was seasonal and local. The mountains grew smaller each hour of each day and the alluvial fans grew broader and thicker. Even if there had been witnesses, these events would hardly have been discerned. Their timetable was protracted and little happened day by day that could be seen.

Beneath the surface of the earth, though, in that sandy area with the juniper stands just in from the sea, other forces were at work and these could have been witnessed had there been men to do so. They were events that cost, in time, tens of thousands of individual creatures their lives.

Beneath the sandy flats were folded layers of variously colored clays. A yellow clay lay on top, lightly sprinkled with recent debris, below that brown clay; in some areas there were thick streaks of blue. Veined through it all were layers of oil-stained sand, buried pools of liquid tar, and pockets of gas. Seams of bituminous material threaded through, and black clay, part petroleum and part inorganic sands, rose and fell within the matrix according to the chances of fold and distortion. It was uncertain land, an area to be known as the Los Angeles basin in a distant future.

One quiet day, when the winds from the sea barely stirred the dust devils that lay sleeping in the sand, when the sun was hot and yellow, a distant grumbling could be heard. It was a discontented sound, a complaining one, as if a mighty force were angry at the obstacles it found in its path. Suddenly, with no more warning than that, a thick stand of junipers seemed to rise straight into the air and then part. For a brief instant the ground that rose with them, still carrying their roots, looked like a round-domed hill, but then it disintegrated as the huge pocket of gas that had been forming seventy feet down exploded upward. The trees scattered in all directions and where flatland and then a fleeting dome of earth had stood there was a hole, nothing more. The sound of the explosion was muffled and there was no fire. The hissing died, the gases joined the atmosphere, and once again internal forces had changed the landscape, although in this case the change was small and of local influence only. Still, a cavity in the earth is a dynamic thing and many forces are summoned into play by its creation.

Within minutes after the explosion occurred, the land began to bleed. The upward thrust of the over-burdened gas pocket had slashed through seams of oil-bearing sand and had ruptured several trapped reservoirs of tar. A thick, black liquid began seeping down the walls of the newly excavated hole and pools formed in the bottom. The winds rose and thin layers of sand rained down only to be absorbed in the pools and then covered with more liquid as the flow increased. Like an osmotic membrane, the walls of the hole drew liquid from the surrounding strata. Quartzite pebbles and igneous boulders tumbled into the growling pools and in places small landslides occurred in the coarse sands. The pool filled, hour by hour, day by day. As veins emptied themselves and their open ends were smothered by the deepening tar, gas followed the channels and surged in below the surface. Worming its way upward, the gas bubbled at the surface in small, tarry volcanoes. Gas burping free into the air knocked low-flying insects down to struggle briefly on the clinging tar swamp. Small rodents exploring along the edges of the pit found the footing uncertain and each day some were caught in collapsing ridges and swept down into the pool. Their struggles were hardly more impressive and no more fruitful than those of the dragonflies and mosquitoes. The fossil treasure of the La Brea tar pits had begun to form.

It did not take many months for the pool to fill, and then overflow. The seeping liquid found open holes, places around tree roots, animal burrows, and other gas evacuations and flowed in to fill these as well. The area was dotted with black splotches but the land was still essentially sandy. Often high winds would scatter sand across the flat and the exposed tar would be covered, made briefly invisible by the crystalline debris. Eventually, though, the grains of sand would pock the surface of the tar with their own weight and then vanish, sinking slowly down to mix with the growing collection of bones that was accumulating near the bottom. For days and sometimes weeks on end the tar would be shiny black again, marked here and there with a newly exploded bubble of gas, until new winds and new wind-borne debris littered the area.

The cow camel stood seven feet tall where her back arched slightly above her rib cage. The top of her head was more than eight feet from the ground as she ambled along, her head thrust forward. As much a llama, really, as a camel, she did not have the pronounced humps of her Asiatic cousins but she was unmistakably of their cut. Her calf stayed close to her, for the survival demands of their species had instilled in them an instinctive alertness, a natural caution. Proof of the predator lies in the movements of the prey.

As they moved out into the open they passed through a loose stand of live oak, then some manzanita. Far off to their right a herd of enormous bison, as high in the hump as the top of the camel's skull, grazed slowly in the late afternoon quiet. Further on, two imperial mammoths, nearly thirteen feet in height, shuffled forward on their pillarlike legs, their heads seemingly weighted down by their enormous incurving tusks.

The powerful sabertooth, about the size of an African lion today, had been resting up in a hackberry grove during the heat of the afternoon. Truculent, small-brained, and aggressive it had been alone most of its life. It did not get along well with others of its kind, or with any other animals for that matter. It attacked what it met and both inflicted and received crippling injuries in many of these encounters.

Now, in the late hours of the sun, it sensed the cow camel and her calf. It rolled over on its side, then onto its belly and watched, head low to the ground. Off in the distance a herd of small pronghorns stood at alert, the herd buck barely two and a half feet tall. They were too swift, though, and the day still too hot. Even if he revealed himself, he knew instinctively, the camel's flight would be hindered by her concern for her calf. His choice was simple, obvious.

Slowly inching forward with his weak hind legs and powerful forelegs folded under him, the sabertooth worked himself to the edge of the hackberry stand. Then he stood and in a second was in open pursuit. He could at least have the calf. The cow camel spotted him immediately and, calling her alarm note, galloped across the flat with her calf bleating piteously in pursuit. It appeared for an instant as if they might outdistance the cat but suddenly the camel's front legs buckled and she plunged forward, then over in an awkward somersault. Her front feet were mired and both legs snapped as she went over. The calf, because of its lighter weight, was able to take two full strides onto the surface of the tar before becoming entrapped. The cow's struggles enabled her to get her head free from the mire but she was doomed, unable to right herself.

The sabertooth was only a few strides behind and in a final leap landed on the stricken camel. His weaker lower jaw swung clear and again and again he stabbed and twisted his incredibly elongated upper canines into the camel's belly and chest. His strokes were powerful enough to splinter bone and the camel's ribs collapsed. The cat's nostrils were far up on his snout, conveniently back and out of the way, and he was able to push his muzzle deep into the gaping wounds his teeth made without having his breathing hindered. The free-flowing blood coursed along corrugations in his upper gums and he sucked and swallowed, sucked and swallowed. He then began to eat.

The calf had died within minutes after the sabertooth had killed its mother, its bleating having summoned a number of spectators to the side of the pool. During the few minutes of furious activity that occurred immediately after the camel became mired, a pocket mouse edged near the pool's outermost seeping and was struck by a rattlesnake. After ingesting its prey the snake slithered across some apparently firm sand and sank out of sight in the tar. A two-foot tall *parapavo* turkey became entrapped at about the same time in another pool nearby and increased the rate at which it sank by its frantic struggles. When only its head remained above the tar a raven landed on some sand nearby and began pecking at the turkey's eyes. When it tried to lift off, the raven found that it, too, was caught and soon vanished beneath the surface.

The sabertooth's perch on the cow camel's belly

kept it clear of the tar during the time it fed. When it was satisfied, though, and turned to leave, it found its hind legs gripped by the viscous trap. Struggling violently, its numb brain barely able to grasp the nature of its plight, it finally pulled itself free. It then turned and stepped off the carcass as if nothing had happened. Its forelegs sank into the tar up to the shoulders and the recently fed sabertooth cat was doomed to die the death of thousands in the greedy La Brea tar pools.

A thousand feet up, eleven incredible *teratornis* circled on their twelve-foot wings. Undoubtedly the largest flying birds the world has ever known, these forty-pound scavengers waited patiently for movement to stop. As the sabertooth's last convulsive kicks ran down his hindquarters (his head was submerged and he had suffocated), the *teratornis* began their descent. They spiraled down until one after another they landed on the exposed portions of the camel, her calf, and the great cat. Before they were ready to lift away, three of them would be caught and their bodies would be gone before the next sunrise. None of the animals in the area seemed to be able to learn the danger the black pools posed and species after species contributed carcasses to the bone collection of the pits.

Just slightly lower on the carrion-eater's pecking order was another great soaring bird, the California condor. Specimens of this species, too, had seen the flight of the camel and her calf, their entrapment, and the sabertooth's attack. While circling high above they had watched the *teratornis* land, feed, and depart leaving three of their kind struggling in the tar. When the remaining eight giants had departed, the condors started their slow, circling glide down. Cautiously one, then another, then two more landed on what remained of the carcasses. All four fed on the still ample remains, one concentrating on a *teratornis* before it was quite dead, and three finally managed to lift away. Only one became trapped. Of the three that managed to get away, one separated from the other two and flew off toward the north. Encountering a strong updraft, it gained in altitude and slanted toward the northeast. Within an hour it was flying over a deeply cut valley with high, predator-proof rock walls, and then began its descent. It came to rest on a bare oak that grew out of a hundred-foot-wide grass-covered ledge a thousand feet up from the canyon floor. It remained on its naked perch for ten minutes, scanning the sky above and the canyon below. Satisfied with its solitude, secure in the belief that it could proceed without disturbance, it spread its wings, caught the wind and kicked free. It circled the canyon twice and came down on a rocky ledge several hundred feet below the canyon's rim. From inside the rocky cave a small downy ball came forward hissing and flapping its stubby wings. Within moments the heads of the two birds were locked together and the adult regurgitated a chunk of saber-tooth tiger flesh. The infant condor withdrew its head from its parent's bill and began to feed. With its peculiar shuffling gait the parent bird moved out of the cave to the rocky ledge overlooking the canyon and stared off into space. Its bright red eyes had a timelessness in them. As windows to its brain they somehow belonged as much to the future and the past as to that particular present.

As it watched, a form drifted in at the end of the valley. The mate circled slowly until it found a convenient draft and then drifted straight down toward the cave. When it was a hundred yards off, the male lifted free of the ledge, fell for a moment and then caught the rising air. Together the two birds rose up, up beyond the rim of the canyon, up until they were twelve thousand feet above their valley. They selected a flyway, a route already thousands of years old to condor and condor ancestral forms and flew toward the south. A roughening in the air told them a storm lay in their path and they climbed to fifteen thousand feet to avoid it. At that altitude they encountered thick clouds. Unable to climb over them, without a chance of flying under them since they reached the ground in the heavy storm weathering the area, the birds curved toward the east, cutting across the front with its potentially dangerous winds. In a valley forty miles to the east they found a quiet area and came to roost. In thirty hours the area would clear and they would return to their own valley carrying more food for their single chick.

Chapter Three

The California condor that flew then, in the time of the mastodon, ground sloth, and sabertooth cat, was not unlike the California condor we know today. It was, almost certainly, an ancestral form only slightly larger in size. We assume *it looked very much like the bird we now know, for so its skeleton would have us believe. There was a major difference, however; it was neither rare nor restricted in range. The pair that carried food back to the chick in the cave when the storm had moved off could have flown fifteen hundred miles to the north, three thousand to the east, and found their kind nesting in appropriate areas. There were condors then nesting in British Columbia and in Florida. Much has happened since.*

The single downy chick in the cave high up in the canyon wall matured under the solicitous care of its parents, separated from them, found a mate, and became a parent himself. There were occasional mortalities among the chicks he fathered and some breeding years were barren, but enough of his kind followed to carry the species on down through the centuries. Subtle changes occurred, favored characteristics became accentuated while less vital ones faded in the genetic pool until the condor that was vanished and a new species evolved. There are hints in bones, to be sure, but the whole story is far too subtle for us to trace. We only know that it happened for we have the results. We understand it imperfectly.

While the condor altered itself and found new ways to survive, great changes occurred on and in the land over which it soared. The camels vanished, the ground sloth, the sabertooth, the mammoth and the mastodon followed. Bison became smaller, and probably more numerous, and the fabulous teratornis disappeared from the skies. A species of condor, two vultures, a caracara, an ancient golden eagle and four other eagle species as well faded away. One by one they melted back into time: the dire wolf, the short-faced bear, a tapir and a lionlike cat that had con-

tended with the sabertooth, they all went. Somehow, though, the condor held on, for there was something there Nature wanted to preserve. Few new species appeared, for there was enough in the old collection worth preserving; but many had to go.

During the period of the condor's meticulously slow transformation, one new species did appear along the coast that would have profound meanings for the condor in the ages that lay ahead. Slowly, from the north, they appeared, not native to the land but migrants who had found good enough reasons to risk the coming. They could not fly, they could run only clumsily, and they had neither fang nor claw. They did have wit, though, more than any other animal, and that outweighed all the other advantages possessed by native species. Man had come bringing his greed, his natural bent for waste, and his open, often untempered hostility.

The first men apparently came across from Asia during the last ice age, when a bridge existed between the two continents. Strangely, they found the coastal regions of Alaska temperate and unglaciated. They moved down into British Columbia and from there south and east. We do not know for certain what they looked like, how they spoke, what they carried with them, or even very much about what they met along the way, but come they did to conquer first one continent and then another to the south.

The first relationship between man and the condor was mystical. The condor soared beyond the spear's throw, beyond the cast of the sling, so he was seldom hunted. He assumed, instead, an aura of legendry that became intensified down through the years. As the cultures of man throughout his range became richer, so did the tales and attributes that had the condor at the center.

The Tlingit people said the condor caused the thunder by flapping its wings, even by moving a single quill. The lightning, they claimed, came from the bird's red eyes. An angry condor, they were sure, was likely to create thunder and lightning until it was able at last to capture a whale to carry off to a mountaintop home.

To the people of the Tsimshian nation the condor was one who carried maidens away and captured the wives of other birds. In one instance, a single condor created a gale with his wings, destroying all other birds around just so it could have the wife of a woodpecker who happened, in this case, to be a thrush.

The Kwakiutl, the Comox, and the Nootka peoples as well feared the thunderbird in their legends as the great abductor. The Kathlamet called him Ikenuwakcoma *and attributed to him similar tendencies. In the south the Hopi named one of the three branches of the eagle clan for the condor and favored the deity* Kwatako *with some of his characteristics.*

The legends grew richer as the centuries passed and the condor, or thunderbird, became a favored subject of artists and craftsmen. In spruce-root basketry, on carved wooden poles, on cave walls, and in the design of pottery, the silhouette of the condor flourished. As the most masterful soaring bird in the sky, as an untouchable, unreachable image in black against the blue and the white, he became a demigod and as such would probably have survived across his vast range. But, other forces were due, and these were to be less benevolent.

From a different direction they came, across a different ocean. They had a greater greed, even, than the earlier men, a far greater sophistication, and guns. What the spear could not reach the musket could. What the darkskinned man all but worshiped, the paler man destroyed. S 1547015

It was in the year 1602 that white man first acknowledged the condor in writing. A Carmelite friar, Father Ascension, recorded a flock feeding on a dead whale in Monterey Bay. His observations were included in an encyclopedic work published in Spain thirteen years later. It was a peaceful observation unlike those that were to follow.

1805: one killed at the mouth of the Columbia River by Captain Clark; 1806: two killed by a hunter in the same area. 1827: two killed by botanist David Douglas near the site of present-day Portland. 1845:

an artist-ornithologist collected another. For each one killed and recorded, thousands were destroyed quietly, privately. Their huge eggs, often four and a half inches long and nearly three inches in diameter, attracted the collectors, and nests were robbed without regard for the fact that one condor lays one egg every two years. The collectors neither knew nor cared that Nature, in designing the condor's ways, anticipated a high rate of survival. Why else would a condor lay but that single egg in twenty-four months, while in the same period a tortoise lays at least two hundred, and a codfish twenty million? But the gatherers could not be bothered with such things. The eggs brought too high a price from museums and private collectors in the East.

The condor, of course, wilted before the attack. It had come too far, was too settled in its ways. By the dawn of the twentieth century, few existed north of central California, none east of the Rocky Mountains. But man's work was not done, even with that. Since then the vise has continued to tighten and today, of the thousands that once knew the skies from Florida to Vancouver Island, fewer than fifty remain, all nesting, when they nest, in a total area of less than 55,000 acres.

In Santa Barbara County, California, there are 1,200 acres in Los Padres National Forest, within the San Rafael Primitive Area. This is the Sisquoc Condor

Sanctuary. North of Fillmore, in Ventura County, there are 53,000 acres designated as the Sespe Wildlife Area, and here are most of the known condor nesting sites. This is what man has left of North America to the condor. This is his share. The bird that flew in ancestral form before man even knew land lay in this hemisphere, the bird that fed its young on the flesh of imperial mammoths and sabertooth cats, this is what has been left to him. It is not at all clear that we will allow him to keep even that. Covetous eyes look in his direction even now. Our greed is not sated, the condor's last chapter may be about to be written.

The promise made to the future by the Archaeopteryx *one hundred and fifty million years ago lives on in the condor today. It remains to be seen if man will allow the promise to be kept.*

Chapter Four

And so the time of the American elephant had passed and the time of the American man had begun. It was a time of hazard, a time for the death of splendor.

THEY WERE ANXIOUS to get back to their chick. They had been away nearly eleven hours and their internal clocks were producing a tension that seemed to bridge the silent gap between them with a naturally coordinated signal. The winds had died down after the storm passed and it was not an ideal time for flight. They were on naked branches, one above the other, in a tall, dead oak far up on the sunburned slope of the valley. From their perches they could look out across several thousand acres of chaparral. Again and again they adjusted their positions, leaning forward as if to fly, but pulled back each time. A condor does not like to launch himself without the assistance of the wind. But, there was no wind and the poststorm cumulus formed high, white mountain ranges against the deep blue of the recently laundered sky.

The female condor, particularly, felt the mounting tension. Echoing deep below her conscious mind was a knowledge of the small posturing entreaties and hissing sounds her chick would now be making. He would be begging food of phantom parents and going through his rituals although no birds stood on the ledge before him offering freshly regurgitated carrion. He, too, had his clock.

Several times she lifted her wings, spread her tail, and felt for a helpful, even encouraging current of air. There was no such encouragement to be had. Finally, she could take the strain no longer. The demands of her parenthood were too great. She lifted her wings straight up, reaching with them nearly five feet above her back. She expanded the feathers of her tail, elevated it as well, straightened her legs, and pushed down hard against the perch. Then, in one coordinated movement, she brought her tail and both wings down sharply, shoving with all her might at the same time. Her full twenty-two pounds were instantly airborne and as she started to lose precious altitude she raised her wings again.

Twelve times in just over four seconds she flapped her wings. Although her wingspan, broad tail, and body surface gave her over twelve thousand square centimeters of loading surface, her weight was so great, nearly a pound and a half per square foot, that the early stages of her flight in calm air were inefficient. After the initial twelve beats though, she was able to glide for a thousand yards, then she beat twelve more strokes to gain altitude. By this time she had passed over the ridge to where a rising thermal from the steep wall beyond surged beneath her. She rocked slightly and then lifted. She banked a few degrees to the left to adjust her direction, caught the thermal again, and curved off in the most magnificent soaring flight to be seen in the world of birds today.

When she flapped, the whooshing sound her wings made could be heard fully a half-mile away. Now, in soaring flight, at ever increasing altitude, the sound was less and was heard by no one but her. It was like a soft wind in a pine tree. Forty percent of each wing was open slot area, finely adjustable to her minutest flight requirements. Her extraordinarily long primary feathers, each an elastic and flexible wing in its own right, turned on their axes and were thrust automatically forward at a slight angle. She was moving at a speed of thirty-five miles an hour and still accelerating. It would be half an hour at least before she would move her wings from the horizontal again.

After passing over a second ridge, she circled once to adjust her bearing. It took her fifteen seconds to complete the full turn, twice as long as a turkey vulture making the same maneuver a thousand feet below. As she completed her turn, she located her mate two hundred feet behind her and to her left. He was completing his turn as she leveled off and he speeded up until they were abreast. Side-by-side, a hundred and fifty feet apart, they headed north. A sea wind coming in from the west splashed against the ridge below and threw a vertical current of air up directly beneath them. By the time they had reached the southern end of their valley their speed had increased to fifty-five miles an hour. At that speed, from an altitude of over ten thousand feet, the two enormous birds began their controlled descent. No observer could miss their similarity to two huge aircraft. Indeed, it is a mistake that has been made.

Slots on their wings' leading edges opened, their

tails dropped, and the spaces between their primaries were adjusted. While still a thousand yards from the entrance to the cave, the male dropped his legs and allowed them to dangle freely; she kept hers tucked up until the last moment before landing. With their wings fully extended and dihedrally up, they swept by the rock ledge once, banked sharply, and approached it again. With tails dropped to the vertical and with five last-minute stop-beats, they came down almost side-by-side. The sound of their landing, a kind of muffled crack, could be heard several hundred feet away. Slowly they folded their wings and, with the female in the lead, they started back into the narrow cave.

Before they had gone more than a few steps they were met by a frantic hissing sound, and then its source, a grayish-brown ball of furlike down. The chick's age could be fixed at just slightly more than two months, since the first black feathers had already appeared on his wings. He was still totally dependent on his parents for food, however, and his demands were insistent and relentless in their frequency. The intensity of their solicitude matched his needs.

Hissing and grunting, the chick pressed his bill up against his mother's. She held hers vertically down, and, turning his head to the side, the chick thrust his whole head into her mouth. She hunched twice and after a unified bobbing motion he withdrew his head with part of a ground squirrel that had been killed on a highway twenty hours earlier. In turn, the male fed the chick with part of a domestic cat that had lost an argument with a rattlesnake two days before, and both adults moved out to the edge of the cave entrance. It was now past six and they longed for their roosting site, where they would remain until well after dawn. They kicked free of the ledge and glided easily down the slope at the foot of the cliff, carving a gentle arc that duplicated the contour of the land, and came to rest on two branches of a dead tree seventy feet above the ground.

As they settled down on their perches, the two silhouetted birds constituted exactly one twenty-fifth of the world's total California condor population. Their posture seemed to indicate that they felt the burden they carried. Their breast feathers touched the branches and their neck feather ruffs were drawn up to their ears to protect their bare necks from the evening cold. Later, after dark had come into the valley, the male would put his head under his wing. His mate would hold her position throughout the night, although her lids lowered shortly after she settled to her roost and she was sightless.

They were not lovely, these birds; in fact, they were nearly ugly. Ungainly on the ground, even gooselike, with bodies as large as a child's, with bare, raw-looking heads of bright yellowy-orange, and with featherless necks of pale gray, they had the look of the vulture, the eater of carrion, the attendant of death. Their feathers were stark, shiny black and white. There were no wondrous shades of electric blue and green-tinged purple found in other birds; in repose they did not even have graceful, curving lines. Only in flight was their beauty apparent, in their incredible, soaring flight.

What they lacked in physical beauty they compensated for in importance. They were together one of eight pairs of their species on this planet capable of reproducing their kind in that year. They were mated for life and each alternate year would work valiantly to brood and raise a single young. They were affectionate with their chick, and with each other. Theirs was an ideal life, except in their relationship with man. They did not kill to live but, rather, removed carrion from the landscape, thereby being part of Nature's plan to keep things neat in her domain. They destroyed nothing, competed with few, and chose their homes in places far from the natural habitats of unnatural man. Still, they were treated as enemies and the attrition had reached a point where the death of a single bird or the failure of a single pair to successfully brood their egg was a staggering tragedy that shook the very stability of the species itself. The two birds that slept in the tree that night were two of the most valuable and important creatures on earth in any but a madman's reckoning.

Chapter Five

THE INTELLIGENCE AVAILABLE to the parent condors was not great, but neither were they hindered by the lack of it. Nature had long ago weighed all the elements of condor survival and found a practical balance. The birds were capable of learning, but could learn no more than was necessary. They were, more importantly, richly endowed with instincts. (The very word *instinct*, though, is enigmatic since it is a catchall for things we do not really understand.) However the instincts that governed their lives worked, they satisfied the birds' needs. They had come in the original condor package along with length of bone, color of feather, and shape of beak. They required no real breaking-in period or special talent for use. They automatically matured with and within each bird and were respectively available at each level of development to fulfill the tasks at hand. Stimuli within or without would give the signal, a chemical interpretation would be made, and the instinctive response would be there.

Some of the instincts were open-ended, slightly adaptable to new and unusual circumstances, but most were relatively fixed, some actually rigid. The condor nest is such a fixed instinct. The condor does not come equipped with the skill to build an elaborate nest and can never learn such a technique. The mated adults are impelled, rather, to locate exactly the right place and then to rely on the simplicity of natural design to contain and protect both egg and chick.

To a condor, a nest is a place more than a thing. It almost always is found between fifteen hundred and forty-five hundred feet above sea level, generally in the life zone known to science as the Upper Sonoran. While an occasional cavelike hollow in an immense tree may be used, the cliff face or boulder pile are preferred.

The adults that returned that day with food for their chick returned to a fairly typical condor nesting site. It was high enough off the canyon floor to allow safe takeoffs on days when the winds were uncooperative. It had good roosting sites nearby and a ledge at the mouth of the cave to aid their chick in his early attempts at flight. The cave interior was two feet high and just slightly over two feet wide. While incubating the egg the parents had the security of closeness, yet were able to move around and adjust their positions. About a third of the actual incubation had been taken over by the male and he had functioned as well in this regard as his mate. They had pushed a few pebbles together in the soft sand floor and, perhaps accidentally, included a little windblown vegetable debris in the pile. That was the grand total of their architectural skill. On this pile the single egg had been laid in mid-March. But the egg was away from wind, virtually secure from predators, and carefully attended by two intense parents. It was enough.

The nesting cave was more than a place to lay an egg and then hatch it. For the condors it was a place to which they would return nearly every day for more than five months. It would be that long before their chick would be free of its protecting sandstone walls with their veins of shiny inclusions. As long as the chick was there it was an anchor point for the adults. It was as if they lived at the end of a long chain that pivoted on a rod planted in the cave floor. Whatever the attractions elsewhere, they would inevitably end up back at the pivot point, responding to ancient signals, directed by the need of another life. Nature had assured herself of a successful continuity within the species by imprisoning each adult in a code and an ethic of natural behavior. Only disturbance in the nesting area could crack the code and smash the pattern, for it is a strange contradiction in condors that while they are bothered relatively little by man elsewhere, in the nesting area they are poised on the edge of hysteria, ready to be triggered by the slightest intrusion. Where their imperturbability is most essential it is almost entirely lacking.

The care the chick received during his five-month lying-in was virtually flawless. Although left without food for nearly two full days on a couple of occasions when storms interfered with the return of the adults, his feeding schedule was fairly constant. On days when he was fed once, the meal was offered regularly between two and five in the afternoon. On occasional days when two meals were offered, the first came before noon. It was all very regular, all very logical, all engineered to provide the young bird with a maximum chance for survival. For the adults to have failed in their duty in any particular would not have endangered their own lives but their species. Nature had thereby provided an urgency to their nesting and brooding behavior by making it a compulsion as strong as their own drive to live. For

Nature it is all the same thing. In examining her wonders we focus our attention on individuals. That is our shortsightedness. To her, species, not individuals, are important.

The incredible clock mechanism of instinct kept the adults, one at a time or together, at the nest for specific periods during the various stages of the chick's development. When the infant bird was still covered by his natal down and most vulnerable to temperature changes, he was brooded constantly, never left alone. When the second down appeared, brooding took place at night only, testifying to his newer and firmer grip on life. When the juvenile feathers appeared, all brooding stopped and visits by the parents were for feeding only.

And so, through the coordinating power of the incredibly complex system of internal communication and organization we call the nervous system, the adult birds were able to produce their young and see him through his hazardous early months. Responding to an intricate pattern, they did all of the right things most of the time, and few enough of the wrong things to assure the payment of their species-oriented debt to Nature. Without even knowing that they possessed them, they passed along to their chick the instincts that would carry on through him to another generation. Each bird flew the full course of life like a great relay race, passing the baton of condor behavior along to the next runner before collapsing with exhaustion. There is a difference to be noted before abandoning the analogy, however. Before the big race starts in intramural athletics, those runners likely to drop the baton are eliminated. There are successive heats that assure the coach of the best available team. Among condors, where the population is exceedingly small, each individual must take the baton. The heat *is* the final race so a dropped baton is a major tragedy.

At the age of 148 days, the chick left the nest and began to follow his parents on ever lengthening forays. The dorsal surfaces of his wings were now fully feathered and his power of flight was remarkable. His parents still fed him regularly, wherever they happened to be in the course of their daily wandering, but the young bird was beginning to explore food possibilities himself as opportunities arose. The parents adjusted their flight patterns somewhat to accommodate the lesser skill of their offspring but each day saw the necessary reduction in mobility shrink. By the time the chick was nine months old, he was no longer a problem worth their serious consideration. Patterns of behavior long in use are not easily discarded, though, and from habit the parents still fed the chick occasionally although the ritual was no longer necessary for his survival. At ten months they still nibbled their full-grown chick affectionately, but the signals prompting the behavior were becoming weaker.

The younger bird was finding interests elsewhere that compensated for his loss and the time came easily when the three birds kicked free of their roost, two to travel north while one, the darker bird without the distinctive white triangular markings beneath his wings, flew south. As he circled free and away he faced an organization of life no less fixed than that which had assured the care he had received during his early months. He would mature for five full years before seeking a mate of his own. His gray neck would phase over into pink-orange and his brown eyes would turn to bright red. Not until these color-coded signals were given would he be able to assume the role of adult and reproducer. Until then he would concern himself with growth and strength and basic survival skills. He had been given his chance by Nature. He had been endowed with breathtaking powers of flight and superb senses to connect his internal world of instincts and glands with the external world of stimuli. His was a coordinated life as he separated from the parent birds that late October morning, one coordinated within himself and one well suited to survive in the forty-by-four-hundred mile swath of California that man had allotted to his kind.

Chapter Six

THE YOUNG CONDOR swung due south along a high ridge, keeping it directly below him for a dozen miles. There was a favorable updraft of deflected sea winds and he was able to soar most of the way. It would be improper, perhaps, to say that he was enjoying himself, for that would imply that he was capable of human emotions, but there was a pleasure principle at work in his actions and behavior. From time to time he dipped and dropped down close to the ridge only to rise again. There was no discernible purpose to these actions, for he was not particularly hungry and was not scanning the valley below the ridge. It was just that he wanted to drop and then beat his way up again. In places his invisible highway itself swooped because of a changing feature in the land structure beneath him and he swooped with it. It was remarkably like a game.

It would be improper, too, to say that he *missed* his parents but he did feel something. There was a change in his world and he was aware of it. For the first time in his life he had no fixed associations. The valley of his birth was a faded memory and the two adult birds that had been his anchor point had swept away with the wind. He was alone and had come to the time of his trial.

It was the natural plan that the young condor would spend the next four years of his life mastering the skill of survival. In so doing he would demonstrate that he had inherited both the complete condor package of instincts that could be passed along to another generation, and the stamina to use them in survival. When both of these were proven, he would breed. When thousands of condors soared over the land it didn't matter very much whether any one bird passed the test or not, for there were always others. However, there was no longer any latitude in the population. It had come to the time in condor history when every bird was needed, every ounce of condor potential was critical.

Just as a seven-year-old boy is puzzled by the attitude of a seventeen-year-old boy toward girls, the juvenile bird would have been puzzled by the attention shown each other by adult birds of the opposite sex. That part of him hadn't been born yet. There were within him a variety of instincts that lay dormant, waiting for their proper time. In their turn, each would unfold like the buds on the branch of a tree and each would then command his attention and direct his life into the channels required. For the moment, though, he had to learn to live and to adapt himself to changing circumstances according to the plan and insofar as his open-ended instincts would permit.

As he swept southward along the ridge, his incredibly sharp eyes picked up movement several miles toward the west at about his own altitude. As an aid to learning, Nature has equipped the condor with a definite curiosity. Condors are interested in what goes on around them, or at least they are impelled to investigate what they don't understand. The dark-feathered juvenile swung to his left, flapping his wings on the bank to steady himself, and quickly caught a rising thermal from a break in the north-south ridge below that permitted a meandering stream to pass carrying waters from the hills down to the ocean. As he swept westward along the stream, the dark spot in the sky before him began to grow.

It was evident that the dark shape had seen the condor as well. It swung in a full circle and then spiraled upward. With more experience, the young condor would have been able to tell from the silhouette that he was approaching a golden eagle, easily his master in the air. For the moment, though, in his ignorance, he accepted the distant climbing shape as another of his kind and flew steadily toward it. Suddenly, the climbing bird changed its shape. The stiff wings of the soaring bird bent and came in close to its body. The force of the bird's flight had brought it nearly overhead, and suddenly, as the wings folded, it dropped. A strange, high-pitched peeping squeal reached the condor just seconds before the great eagle itself. The two birds didn't actually collide but they came so close that the condor was knocked sideways by the rush of air. He had had no experiences, no training that had taught him how to cope with this situation. He had never been the object of a hostile act and had no reserve to call on. He reacted in the only way he could, he panicked. In its plunging flight the eagle had dropped several hundred feet below the condor before checking its fall. It had actually tumbled over once (or so it appeared from the ground) before swooping in an exquisitely controlled arc to begin the ascent. As a soaring bird the condor knows no peers. In aerobatics, though, the golden eagle far exceeds any skill the condor can ever know.

A more experienced condor would have dropped down as close to the ground as possible at the first sign of trouble from above. By hugging the ground he would have denied the eagle the one thing it most needed, maneuvering room. But, gripped by panic, not fully aware of the trouble that was developing, and crippled by inexperience, the condor rose higher, steadied himself and flew on. Within seconds the eagle stooped again and veered to the side, just inches away from the condor's head. Again the juvenile stuttered in his flight and nearly fell from the sky. Awkwardly he regained level flight and banked toward the south, but again the eagle swooped. This time, as the eagle passed it rolled and swept across the condor's belly upside down. Its talons brushed the condor's belly feathers but did no real damage.

By the time the eagle had made four passes, the condor was blind with terror. He was barely able to regain level flight after the fourth pass and, again testifying to his inexperience, he attempted to add altitude. For the fifth time the eagle stooped, swept in close, and taunted the condor. Inspired by its own skill it actually brushed the condor as it swept by at a speed of seventy miles an hour. A few feathers drifted slowly down into the valley below. On the fifth pass the condor reached the point of panic that can paralyze an animal and he half-folded his wings. He began falling. It wasn't exactly an uncontrolled plunge, but neither was it the magnificently coordinated flight that even this young bird was capable of. It was something halfway between. The bird's survival would depend on his ability to recover in a matter of seconds, his ability to respond to this new situation. The condor's bearing surface was drastically altered by the half-folded wings and the rising air was unable to support the weight of the bird in the rapidly accelerating plunge. When he was two hundred feet off the ground he stretched his wings out to their fullest, dropped his tail, caught the air and leveled off. He came to earth in a clearing below the ridge. The eagle, a young tiercel who grew in skill with each of these practice sessions, swooped low overhead, calling in his taunting little-bird voice, and disappeared over the ridge beyond. He had meant the condor no harm but was angry at his unwillingness to respond. The game would have been more fun if two had played.

The condor was badly flustered by his misadventure. He wasn't anxious to take off again and began investigating the clearing in which he had made his impromptu landing.

In his characteristic slouching walk, swinging his body from side to side, bobbing his head backward and forward, he took a few steps, stopped, looked around, and made a half-dozen piglike grunts before taking several more steps. A raven took off from a bush nearby and as it flew overhead the condor crouched low and hissed. He was in no mood for other birds at the moment. In ten minutes he progressed about a hundred yards, arriving at a steep slope that dropped away to a small pool cradled in a jumble of fallen rock. Switching to his other gait, he spread his wings and hopped down the slope, flapping his wings on alternate hops. He still stopped frequently to scan the strange area and to check the ridge for the eagle's return. By the time the condor had reached the pool, the eagle was nearly twenty miles away and had found himself another condor on which to practice his techniques.

It would, perhaps, be more satisfying to the image people have of carrion eaters if the condor were a filthy bird but, in fact, he is extremely neat and clean. He bathes as often as practical and pays very careful attention to the grooming of his feathers. The bathing ritual of the condor is very important to him and is relatively fixed in style.

As the young bird approached the pool he stopped by a small bush and ripped off a twig. He held it in his beak for several seconds before dropping it. He cocked his head and looked at it, picked it up again, and took several more steps. Again he dropped it, studied it lying on the ground, stepped on it with one foot, and stripped the leaves off. Satisfied with what he had accomplished (which to the human observer may have been nothing at all but to the condor may have been an important displacement activity to channel off emotional energy) he moved to the edge of the pool.

At the edge he looked around several times before wading in a few steps. Standing in water about three inches deep he bent low and nibbled at the surface, raised his head quickly as if he had heard something, nibbled again and swallowed. The dipping and nibbling went on for a minute or two, then, unaccountably, he retreated from the water, looked around, and hissed. He found a small piece of bark nearby and worried it for several minutes, tossing it, stepping on it, pushing it around in the dirt with his beak. Then, somehow, the excess was used up. The memory of the disturbing encounter with *Aquila*, the golden eagle, was forgotten as a specific event. It was, however, carefully tucked away as an experience and would provide an episode-oriented reflex the next time he encountered a golden eagle aloft.

Usually, among adult birds, an afternoon bath is more thorough than the morning ablution. However, even though it was still before midday, the young bird was somewhat at odds with the world and the bath gave him something concrete to do. He wandered back into the pool to where the water was five inches deep and sank down until his breast was submerged. He quickly ducked his head under, bringing it out sharply and throwing water over his back. He repeated the action several times, then extended his neck flat along the surface and swung his head back and forth. As a final step he extended his wings, squatted down, flapped his wings three times, stood up and walked out of the pool. His total bathing time had consumed less than ninety seconds.

Once out of the pool he stood up to his full height, flapped his wings vigorously, then shook until the sand around him was pocked with little spots of mud. He left the poolside and began casting around for a suitable sunning platform. Nearby was a huge boulder that had tumbled off the ridge above during a seismic disturbance several hundred years earlier. It was ideal for his needs and in a series of hops accompanied by wing flapping, he made it to the top and there stood with his wings spread wide. He altered his position from time to time, raising his wings high over his back and shifting his position in relation to the sun. Then, again, he spread his wings wide and went through the same series of turns.

A condor cannot consciously know the importance his feathers play in his life, but he instinctively knows to care for them. It all amounts to the same thing. The preening consumed the final hour of his first morning entirely free of his parents. Feathers were nibbled rapidly in each successive area of his body. Several times he let his outstretched wings sag until they draped around him on his perch atop the boulder. Four times he shook his rear end, rather like a duck, and rolled his head and looked at the silent blue sky above. It was all very matter-of-fact, all very easy. Yet, here was an instinct in play that was vital to his well-being. At the altitudes he flew, in the mountain fastnesses he retreated to, having feathers in good repair was essential for the warmth they provided. His magnificent, breathless, soaring flight, too, demanded clean, well-tended feathers for its execution. What appeared to be largely a casual action was in fact a survival skill. How much of it he knew instinctively and how much of it was learned from his parents we will never know. The distinction didn't matter to him at all.

The young condor's first half-day alone had been eventful and meaningful. He had learned a valuable lesson, that he was second in power in the sky to the golden eagle, and he had been able to launch himself into a normal life routine, including bathing and preening, without an adult at hand to set the example. He had many other lessons to learn but there was a matter of immediacy at hand. As he completed his sunning and preening he was aware of a new call. He was hungry. Instinctively he knew there would be no adult with regurgitated morsels to offer, and no other bird to guide him to a carcass. Suddenly, very suddenly, he was alone and whether or not he survived would now depend on his ability to locate and claim suitable food. The ubiquitous berries, seeds and bugs that satisfied the life needs of so many other species of birds would not solve his problem. His was a specialized need. He had to find the place where death had overtaken another animal. For only on the trail of death could his life continue.

Chapter Seven

ALOFT AGAIN, THE YOUNG CONDOR began scanning the ground below for signs of food. Several times he circled an area in slowly descending spirals but took off again in a slanting line upward when the signals disintegrated under closer scrutiny.

His superb eyesight told him more about his surroundings than all of his other senses combined. Each of his eyes was bigger than his entire brain and could quickly evaluate the distance, shape, size, brightness, color and intensity, three-dimensional depth and movement of an object; all of this while passing over it at a height of fifteen hundred feet at a speed of nearly sixty miles an hour. Although the structure of his eyes would show an anatomist his links with a reptilian past, they were now distinctly bird eyes, among the acutest in the world.

About fifteen miles from his bathing pool the young condor spotted a dead squirrel in an open area on a casual slope. The area was suitable for both landing and taking off and he spiraled in. Hopping toward the carcass with his wings outspread, he hissed at imaginary foes and stood over his prize turning his head from side to side. A squirrel is poor food for a condor, far below the carcasses of deer and calves on the preference scale, but the young bird was hungry. And, as it is with all young animals, his hunger was raw and impatient.

The squirrel was not fresh and its hide had softened considerably. The condor opened it without difficulty but before he could feed he noted movement in some brush nearby. Two ravens were on the ground pecking around in some debris and as they emerged into the open the condor hissed violently and flew at them. The sight of the great black bird descending on them was too much for the smaller birds and they took off without hesitation. They did, though, voice their violent disapproval of his behavior.

As the condor wobbled back to his prey he saw still another movement further down the slope. He instinctively sensed danger and stopped to watch. The tannish-gray form of the coyote was instantly recognizable and triggered responses learned from his parents shortly after he had begun accompanying them on their forays. Long before he was in any danger, and with pronounced haste, he ran across the clearing in little bounding leaps with his wings outstretched. He was soon airborne and circled overhead, craning downward as the coyote approached his prize. No sooner had the small brush wolf begun to sniff the squirrel carcass than a huge female golden eagle swept in over the ridge. Before the coyote had time to snarl the bird hit him. It was over in an instant. The bird's talons closed over his spine and severed it. The eagle stood hovering over the still twitching body of the coyote shrouding it with her wings. The young condor had beaten away and caught a rising current at the first sight of the golden bird. He was well away before the coyote was dead.

During the early hours of his first free day the condor had been operating largely over areas between one thousand and three thousand feet above sea level, between the Lower and Upper Sonoran life zones. His flight carried him over chaparral regions of stiff-branched, small-leaved shrubs, over sagebrush areas and mixed woodlands and finally over thick stands of conifers. The varied habitats provided the animals below with a wide range of ecological situations and there were many species to fill the available niches. Mule deer were the largest of the wild animals, unless the few head of feral horses and cattle are to be counted, and the rare mountain lion the most awe-inspiring. Bobcats, coyotes — occasionally crossbred with wild dogs — skunks, opossums, weasels, ring-tailed cats, badgers, fox, gophers, ground squirrels, rabbits and jackrabbits, and a host of small rodents filled out the list of mammals. A wide variety of birds and a good population of snakes and lizards occupied each zone. The condor's survival depended in no small part on his ability to adapt himself to each of these creatures, for during the course of his wanderings he would meet most of them in a variety of situations. Few were natural enemies, but many could be openly hostile if approached the wrong way or at the wrong time. His great size and the sounds of his flight would be intimidating to many (and he would soon enough come to know which they were), but would be ignored by others. It was the latter group that was most critical to his well-being.

After surrendering his squirrel to the coyote, who in turn gave his life to the golden eagle, the condor swept across two intersecting valleys before locating another potential meal. Down the slope of the second valley, almost at the bottom, six condors were gathered over the carcass of a young doe. Three wild dogs had run the doe to ground the night before and had fed off one hindquarter, leaving the rest to the scavengers.

The six condors hunched over the carcass hissing and threatening one another and a ring of eight turkey vultures that stood off at a cautious distance to wait their turn. Beyond the vultures the ravens gathered and muttered to themselves, expressing their discontent at the pecking order Nature had established.

The young condor circled and landed amid the vultures, scattering them in all directions. They closed their ranks behind him as he hobbled toward the carcass. The condors already there raised their heads and stared at him as he approached. Several hissed and worried before going back to their meal. He shouldered his way in but was quickly driven off by another juvenile. Again he worked his way in and managed to grab a beakful before being driven off again. It was not a peaceful meal but he did manage to eat his fill before being driven off for the last time. He was the only bird on the carcass born that year and his lack of experience and resulting lack of authority showed all too plainly. Condors, like almost all animals, will readily bully another of their kind when food is involved.

It took an exceptionally long run with wings flapping for the young bird to get off the ground. He had eaten his fill and suffered, as all condors and vultures do, a marked decrease in mobility when glutted. He did finally manage to get airborne but then had to beat furiously until he caught an updraft on the far side of the ridge. He soared for a few hundred yards and came down on a dead tree with several heavy, naked branches. He began preening his feathers again almost immediately and long before nightfall settled down to sleep. He awoke twice, as two other condors settled on lower branches. He hissed quietly, almost sheepishly it would seem, but neither adult bird paid attention. As the shadows in the valley thickened into darkness the young condor slept. He had survived his first day and learned many lessons. He had observed well during the weeks afield with his parents and was responding effectively to each new learning situation that arose. The signs all pointed to his survival. His package was complete enough. He would carry it through to another generation.

Chapter Eight

THE YOUNG CONDOR AWOKE shortly after sunrise, following a somewhat uneven night's sleep. He was still an uncertain bird. He hunched his shoulders, shook his head, and looked around. The two adult birds were still asleep on the branches below him and he settled down again for several minutes. Far below, the westward-slanting morning shadows were shortening and the color intensity in both the sky and the valley were changing. Morning sounds drifted up to him as the last of the night animals found cover and the first of the day creatures emerged from hiding. A heavily burdened great horned owl beat its way toward a stand of timber. Hanging from its breast was the head of a long-tailed weasel. The two hunters had met in the night and as its final act the weasel had sunk its teeth into the owl's chest. The bird had been able to reach it with one taloned foot and had crushed it there but the weasel had clung on even after death. Working through the night the owl had been able to tear the weasel's body away, but not its head. Like a gruesome badge, it would hang there until it rotted off. In time the owl would learn to accommodate its timing and its flight to the new burden.

The movement below and the passing of two sharp-shinned hawks overhead excited the young condor and he began readying himself for flight. He stood up on the limb to his full height and craned his neck as if to rid himself of kinks. He balanced on one leg and stretched the other out as far as it would go, repeating the action on the other leg and then, quite suddenly, he was ready for flight. Balancing forward on his perch, moving his tail up and down, he spread his wings. The wind was right and he kicked free, fell along the shape of the land for a few dozen yards, and then rose. His ascent was steady and he flapped his wings fewer than a dozen times before reaching a thousand feet. He wobbled slightly at fifteen hundred feet as an intersecting thermal caused a small turbulence, then rose higher. At an altitude of one mile, well beyond the domain of shadows, free in the new sunlight, against a clear blue sky, he climbed. Evenly, steadily, he soared and at a mile and a half above the valley he leveled off. It was cool, quiet and indescribably clean. It is, perhaps, the cleanliness of the altitudes that would be most foreign to land-bound animals, the lack of clutter, of extraneous sound, and of debris, the utter freshness of it that would seem the strangest. Men feel the exhilaration of this new, clean world when they climb a mountain or soar silently in a glider. Perhaps the condor does too, for the young bird flew aimlessly, freely, going nowhere in particular, staying higher than was practical for him if he sought a morning meal. Perhaps the condor, too, can bathe his condor soul in the clean, fresh air of the altitudes. This community of spirit, if it exists, does not depend on manlike qualities in the bird, but the bird in us.

As he moved along with the high air currents, he passed over two other condors who swept diagonally across his course several thousand feet below him. He spotted them, swept in a wide circle to study them, but didn't attempt to join them or to close the intervening gap. The experience with the golden eagle was still too much with him.

After the other condors had passed out of sight

(and at the speeds condors fly that is done very quickly) he continued in his circular flight pattern, altering its circumference several times until it became a fairly tight turn. Then, in a slow spiral, he started down. When he was fifteen hundred feet up he leveled off again and flew along the line of a north-south ridge. Several miles ahead the ridge broke up and descended rapidly to a flat plain strewn with the rubble that had been the ridge's continuing extension before an earthquake shook it down centuries earlier. With a sweeping descent he flew beyond the end of the ridge, out over the plain, past the debris, circled in a wide arc, dropped, and sailed in the mouth of the canyon at an altitude of five hundred feet. He came to earth near a pool shimmering silver in the morning sun. He had been free of his perch for less than an hour, and gone a mile and a half into the sky, exerting very little real effort, and was nearly forty miles away from where the sun had found him.

He drank briefly from the pool and had barely begun to worry a shiny pebble he found on the open sand when a shadow swept across the flat. Instinctively the young bird ducked and hissed. He half-opened his wings and turned his head from side to side. The shadow swept across again and vanished beyond a pile of boulders. He could hear the muffled crack and whoosh of another condor landing. He stood his ground and waited. Just beyond the boulders that crowded in on the pool's edge he could hear the bird moving. Suddenly it appeared on the highest boulder, wings spread, standing out stark and black against the sky. The young bird looked up and recognized the newcomer as a juvenile like himself, a bird without the white underwing markings. The two birds studied each other, one on the sand, the other twenty feet higher, on the rock jumble's highest spot, both with their wings spread. Neither made a hostile move or sound for the newcomer, too, was a bird of the year, newly alone and equally uncertain. Slowly, the young condor on the sand flat beside the pool lowered his wings and almost immediately the newcomer began hopping down, boulder by boulder, steadying himself at each giant step with his widespread wings. He soon joined the first bird on the open sand and cautiously approached. The earlier arrival held his ground and waited.

The two birds came together and after a moment's hesitation began nibbling each other, exhibiting, we can believe, a degree of affection. For each it was the first intentional social contact since separating from their parents. Their previous contacts with other condors had been accidental, at roosting sites and food sources, and had been brief, forced, and with other purpose. This contact had no purpose other than the desire to be with others of their own kind.

The newcomer realized a slight psychological disadvantage in being the second to arrive at the pool. It wasn't so much a matter of territorial claims, as it is with other animals or even with nesting condors, but there was a slight advantage working for the first to arrive. Slowly the newcomer relaxed as the nibbling of each other's feathers continued. The sun, now high and slanting into the valley, glistened off the sandstone rock jumble, reflected off mica chips, and splashed on the two young birds. They shone black, oily and metallic, and, as they moved in relation to the sun, curiously blue. For moments, from some angles, they seemed almost beautiful.

The whole business of beauty, of course, is relative not to varying standards but to application. These two male condors would in the course of their travels encounter scores of other bird species. Near lakes and marshes they would meet spectacularly colored and iridescent wood ducks, baldpates and buffleheads. Daily they would sight ring-necked pheasants, exotic imports from China, quail, chukar partridge from India, a variety of pigeons, rails and gallinules. Shore birds would cross their range and owls would emerge from woods. Hummingbirds and swifts would variously hover and dart, kingfishers and woodpeckers dive and rattle. All around them and beneath them species after species would display their finery and their sexual wares. Yet, for the condors, all other species would be ashes, dry-feathered dust, for they were blind to our concept of beauty, alive only to that which would induce their mating interest. The small, sociable nibbling at the water hole engaged in by the two immature males was part of this, representing an eagerness to approach and a willingness to contact birds of their own feather. Neither would approach with any interest or nibble a bird of living diamonds and gold; for them beauty, if we may use that word, had a more practical application.

As the two immature condors displayed their social senses to each other, worrying small twigs and pebbles they found together on the sand, and finally bathing a few feet apart in the small, clear pool, other creatures with other plans moved nearby. The pile of boulders where the newcomer had first appeared to the young condor was much more than a random hill of mineral debris. It was a thriving community. A family of whiptail lizards lived in a small cavity and a western rattlesnake, dark brown and blotched with black, had a deeper hole. A small but successful population of gray-black tiger salamanders with yellowish spots was scattered beneath piles of vegetation where it gathered windblown and rotting in places where the rocks formed random hollows. Several families of dusky-footed wood rats had traditional homes in the jumble and each member worried constantly about the rattlesnake, the coyotes that visited the area regularly and the red-tailed hawks that nested nearby. They retreated to their small wood-stick homes at the first sign of danger, although many were their aggressive neighbors who could and would huff and puff and blow their homes down.

Undisputed resident master of the rock pile was a large and tawny female bobcat. She had borne six litters in the rock pile and was a fixture in the area, known to all other inhabitants. She moved silently and swiftly and always managed to feed the kittens she bore from the living larder of the boulder community above the pool. Through the years she had deprived many hundreds of lesser creatures of their lives. She was the thinner, the culler of the less swift, the not-so-sure. As the two young condors engaged in their social play below the rocks, the bobcat moved down a familiar path nearby. Nine California quail were hunting for seeds and insects on a flat area near the rocks, behind a boulder and out of sight of the condors. A handsome male with his bobbing crown plume and distinctive black and white face markings barely had time to give the rallying cry. *Quer-ca-go! Quer-ca* — and he was being carried off in the bobcat's jaws. It was that simple, that soon over.

The rush of the cat, the interrupted alarm call of

the quail, and the flushing of the rest of the flock were quickly communicated to the two young condors. "Trouble! Trouble! Trouble!"—it was a message clear and urgent. It spread throughout the entire area and each creature responded in the way best suited to its own survival tactics.

The newcomer responded even more quickly than the young condor. As an even younger bird he had been present at a carcass when a bobcat had rushed some birds nearby and taken a large crow who should have known better than to wander so close to a pile of rubble without checking first. With a grunt, the newcomer was hopping along the flat with wings outspread and head thrust forward. Before the abandoned condor knew what had happened, the newcomer was airborne and flapping for altitude. He circled only once, in time to see his friend hopping along the ground, and was gone. The young condor was off the ground and circling a hundred feet over the boulder pile no more than thirty seconds after the newcomer had vanished over a higher hill beyond. But the separation was enough. The young condor did not pursue his new friend. They would meet again and would perhaps one day compete for the attention of a female. In a population so small, it is likely that each California condor left in this world gets to know all others of his kind. In the eyes of some humans this might appear to be a perfect population size. In the eyes of Nature it is too small for safety. Had the bobcat taken a young condor instead of a quail, the species would have been further jeopardized. The quail population is constructed to withstand such attrition. Nature, thoughtfully, made the bobcat fonder of quails than of condors. This fact works to everyone's advantage, even the quails', for the strength of the species is insured by constant thinning. Occasionally a healthy bird with something important within him for future generations falls prey, but more often a lesser specimen is the victim. It is all in the plan, the plan that includes the condor as well, and the plan works.

Chapter Nine

The cycle of seasons and years spun on, carrying everything in the condor's world with it. His journey into maturity was as inexorable as the planet's course, and each was a part of the other. His link with the world and the cosmos was as firm and real as his ties with the past. Only his lines into the future were uncertain, for his species remained poised on the brink of oblivion throughout the years of his immaturity. Men of exceptional goodwill and with an extraordinary capacity for moral responsibility voiced their concern, and his plight was lumped together in a limited public conscience with the perilous position of a thousand other species of wildlife around the world.

ALTHOUGH THE CONDOR as an individual bird was known to anxious men who watched him through powerful field glasses, recording his travels and noting his growth with satisfaction, and although his range lands were patrolled by salaried men who had vowed to protect his kind from willful intrusion, he knew nothing of it. He was locked up within the limited daylight of his bird-size brain, responding to each moment and each experience as his species always had. For him there was no census, no recorded rate of reproduction or attrition, only food and its getting, wind and its value, storms and their hazards. On the undersides of his wings there was a hint of white, a promise of large triangular markings that would soon appear and announce his capacity for reproduction. When that time arrived, everything that had gone before would have a purpose.

Few days in his life were uneventful. The seeking and claiming of food had sharpened his powers of observation, increased his skill at low-level flying, and given him a growing air of authority suited to a male nearing his maturity. He was no longer chased off carcasses but held his own against all but a few patriarchs in the condor world. Like all of his kind he continued to show deference to some other species, as he always would. The golden eagle, the great *Aquila*, was his master on land and in the sky. The coyote, the mountain lion and the bobcat continued to intimidate him and his reluctance to challenge them when they appeared was a factor in his survival.

Cattle, deer and horses remained high on his food preference list. Man's increased skill in animal husbandry and veterinary science made the supply of carcasses from domestic stock somewhat smaller than the condor's antecedents had known but still there was enough. Small carnivores trapped for their skins, shot for sport, or destroyed as vermin provided occasional food but their naked carcasses were more often discarded in places unsuited to his feeding habits. Although he occasionally fed on a coyote or a bobcat he could perceive no irony. Such intellectual sophistications were beyond his reach. He accepted food as food and didn't concern himself with its source or the reasons behind its availability to him as carrion.

Technically a bird of prey, although he did not actually prey on living animals, he worked under a decided handicap. Whereas the owls, the hawks and the eagles and their kin could carry food off to high and secluded places to eat in safety and at their leisure, he was forced to eat where he found his food.

The other predatory birds have talons and powerful feet that can close over objects of reasonable size and carry them off. He was flat-footed, with feet designed by Evolution for walking and standing only. The legends of condors flying off with everything from men to whales in the talons they do not have are legion and many believe them even today. In simple fact, a condor cannot fly off with a mouse, for he cannot even grasp it. When feeding he can hold a carcass down by pressing on it with a foot while tearing at it with his beak but there the utility of his feet stops. This simple fact requires that he work harder, much harder, than other flesh-eating birds. There were days when the young condor went hungry.

In his third year, while flying low through a sparsely wooded valley, he spotted the carcass of an ancient horse near some brush on an easy slope. He curved in a tight circle and flew over the carcass a second time. There was a dead tree a few hundred feet east of the find and he settled onto its top branch to survey the scene. There was no movement in the valley except for a few lizards in a rockslide but there was a vehicle, a jeep, parked several hundred yards down the slope. He had often seen these small dusty machines and had seen the men who controlled them, but had never learned to associate them with danger. The vehicle was immobile, tight against a large bushy outcropping beside a small stream. He worried about it for a few minutes, preened a few feathers to dissipate the energy his anxiety occasioned, and finally decided it was safe. He kicked free of his perch and flew straight to the carcass.

He landed easily and walked to the horse. He spread his wings, hopped once, and landed on the animal's bloated belly. He couldn't note with any understanding that a bullet hole was centered on the white flash on the grizzled old horse's forehead, nor could he observe with comprehension that the animal's hide had been slit in a number of places to ease his task. He missed, as well, the tire and drag marks that showed plainly that the dead horse had been dragged up the slope behind the jeep. The most important fact he missed was that a crude but effective fence had been set up around the carcass, connecting the obstructive brush and rock outcroppings that littered the area. He had landed in an arena, designed and built for a special purpose. As soon as he had eaten his fill he would automatically be the prisoner of the men in the jeep at the bottom of the slope.

Horse flesh was a favorite food and the slits in the hide of the newly dead animal made his feeding easy. He glutted himself, working rapidly against the intrusion experience had taught him would not be long in coming. In less than fifteen minutes two other condors approached the area and, made secure by the sight of the younger bird eating, circled in on the carcass without first landing on a vantage point to survey the scene. The carcass was large enough so that there was no appreciable squabbling. The three birds fed together and became so engrossed that they didn't notice the first sign of movement down by the parked jeep. Two men started up the slope, one of them carrying a canvas bag.

When the men were about three hundred feet off, one of the older birds, the second to land on the carcass, saw them and grunted his alarm. He turned and ran awkwardly down the slope to get the wind under him. Before he could lift off he ran into the fence and collapsed against it. He sat there, his wings askew, looking foolish and ineffective. The other mature bird and the young condor followed his example and piled into the fence near him. The movement of the men up the slope panicked the birds and in urgent haste they righted themselves and hobbled up the slope and then started down again. Three times they piled into the fence, unable because of the weight of the food they had consumed to lift off in the limited space allowed them. They were trapped by their meal.

The sight of the men climbing over the obstruction into the penned area further terrorized the three birds. They careened into the fence, tried to crash through bushes too thick to allow the passage of a sparrow, and collided with each other. The young condor was no more at a disadvantage than the others. Even their many years had not taught them how to react to this situation.

What happened next was a blur for the young bird. He saw two of the men closing in on him, blocking him into a corner of the pen. As he rushed to get past them, a cloth bag settled over his head. In the dark he was helpless and came to a stop. He felt firm hands grasp his wings and pin them together over his back, heard voices, felt himself lifted off his feet and placed on the ground upside down. He grunted and moaned but quickly stopped his struggling. There was no direct pain associated with the men's activities but the fear he felt hurt almost as much. Even if his head hadn't been covered he would not have understood the long tweezers that prodded in between his feathers in search of parasites or the thermometer that was slipped into his vent. The few feathers that were pulled would not be missed, and the injury to his dignity would not be crippling.

His misadventure was soon over. He was left lying in the dust and when the bag was removed from his head a few minutes later the men were starting away down the slope. The fence on the downhill edge of the pen had vanished and the other birds stood nearby, blinking foolishly in the sun.

None of the birds could appreciate that the examination they had been subjected to could supply science with information that, in combination with other painfully extracted data, might work toward the survival of their species. For them it had been a thoroughly distasteful episode. All wild animals, and a good many domestic ones, are badly frightened by any hint of restraint. Complete freedom of movement is the very essence of being wild. There is an atavistic dread in being held immobile. Too often in a world of carnivore-prey relationships it means being caught, probably to be eaten.

It didn't take the birds long to recover their composure. They were soon off down the slope, grunting with each wing-flapping hop, and then were off, comfortably resting on the rising cushion of air that bunched up beneath them as they rose over the ridge beyond the stream. They didn't look back.

Having shared the most disquieting adventure of his life with the two adult birds, the young condor stayed with them. They rose high over the next valley, strung out in an approximate line, and climbed over a mile into the sky. Twenty miles east they settled into a high meadow where a clear stream ran and bathed there and drank quantities of the near freezing water. After their preening (the two adult birds nibbled each other's feathers but didn't invite the younger bird to participate) they rose off again and flew north. A storm front was pivoting in from the west, starting a southward swing. The birds rose to seven thousand feet to avoid some particularly disturbing turbulence and as the young condor beat forward his temporary companions veered west.

Then, seven thousand feet above the mountainous earth, with black clouds building up on all sides, out of sight, scent and sound of all of the billions of living creatures with which he shared his planet, the young condor was once again alone. There is no solitude on earth the equal of that above a mass of storm clouds. There silence is a sound, nothingness an object, and aloneness a social state that crowds in on a single organism and possesses it. The young condor began his descent, down through the clouds since there were no passages open in view. No one saw him come down, no one saw him settle in the dead oak in the valley and huddle against the storm. Millions of other creatures felt the wind and the rain and heard the symphony of their fury, but no one and nothing thought about the condor alone in the tree, a bird on his way to his maturity, carrying within him the treasure of the eons, one fiftieth of the genetic potential of his kind left on earth.

Chapter Ten

THE CONDOR BANKED, and wobbled slightly as he slipped in over the ridge and dropped down into Sespe Canyon. His high-altitude pass above the Topatopa Mountains had been uneventful but his senses, senses we cannot really begin to understand, told him that something was about to happen. He broke his flight and settled onto a ridge of flat, open rock that jutted out shelflike high up on the canyon wall. Although only seventy miles northwest of Los Angeles's hybrid urbanity, the land he surveyed was a Pleistocene environment. The high, craggy walls hemmed the valley in like a lost world and the scrub-choked valley floor was all but impassable to alien species. Here a small bit of the truly primitive had persisted against incredible odds and here the condor was most at home.

There had been a storm far at sea, a violent interplay of opposing winds and moisture-laden air, and the whole region was in a turmoil of change and adjustment. Weather is important to all wildlife in varying degrees but to the condor, whose avenue is the wind, it is a matter of critical significance. Living as he does at the very margin of a continent, he is always alert, critically attuned to changes that can not only be troublesome but dangerous. There are times when even the condor must stay out of the sky and such times should not come upon him suddenly, for there are places where a condor must not come to earth.

The storm at sea edged the wind source around the compass in a clockwise direction. It had shifted from the sea to the north and was headed to the northeast when the condor sensed the potentially critical change and sought the canyon that time had taught him would be safe. As he settled on his sun-baked perch, the plateau high was bunching up just a few degrees north of east. The region of high pressure covered a vast area and rose many miles above the earth. The sky was clear, the light strangely crystalline and ominous, as if to warn the world that the high-massed pressure area would soon start bleeding off close to the earth's surface.

There is ample evidence to show that even men can feel a heightening tension when barometric pressure undergoes a significant change, and they were not conceived of as creatures who need concern themselves with the winds. How much more sensitive must a condor be! How much more alert to change must be a creature envisioned originally as a denizen of three vertical miles of sky!

The condor paced back and forth nervously. He had been interrupted at his feeding by the silent signals and he was dissatisfied. He did not have the fullness that usually followed a feast and left him feeling well and secure. He had not had time to seek water to bathe in or drink and he felt untidy and incomplete. Some of his body feathers were awry and his feet were caked with gore and sand. He moved abruptly, turning left and then right, not quite sure of what he wanted to do.

Two other condors came into view. One swept by at low altitude, fully thirty feet below the top of the ridge, while the other dropped almost straight down onto the shelf not more than ten feet away. The earlier arrival was too on edge to tolerate the invasion and flew at the newcomer hissing violently. Although an older bird, the invader flopped off into space, banked, and veered across the canyon, seeking a more hospitable perch. He, too, was preoccupied with the coming change and was not inclined to expend his energy on a sordid and meaningless squabble, not while the Santa Ana winds were threatening.

The temperature on the valley floor was over one hundred and ten degrees Fahrenheit and most of the larger animals were bedded down, waiting for the relief of early evening. Within an area of two square miles, mule deer, black bear, a single mountain lion and several bobcats were hunkered under thick vegetation and overhanging rocks, fighting the heat. The snakes and lizards, too, were hidden away, for the direct sun was capable of killing them in a few minutes. Those few lizards that remained at large darted swiftly across open spaces in their endless quest for seventy-two degrees, their optimum operating temperature. It was still, hot and still, for even the smaller birds had sensed the coming winds and had settled into sheltered areas. All singing had stopped and only a quizzical peep was heard from this bush and that. The world of Sespe Canyon waited for the assault it had known before. In a way the canyon was a parent of the wind, for it was a major feature of the land and helped to shape the weather it suffered.

The first sign came as a single dust devil that pirouetted to life on top of a flat rock and flung dry leaves and bits of sand around it into an upward spiral. The small particles spun, dissipated, and vanished. But another devil came to life nearby and then another. Soon a soft rustling could be heard on all sides, as the floor of the canyon began to feel the spill that slipped in over the ridges, snaked down the hot stone walls, and poured into the oven. Faster it came, in ever increasing quantity, as the plateau high ruptured and poured its contents out across the broken ground. The Santa Ana winds had begun. Dust devils failed aborning as gusts of horizontal wind reached thirty miles an hour. As the steady wind increased to thirty, the velocity of the gusts rose to fifty and then seventy, and vegetation clinging precariously to rugged ledges and walls bent, loosened, and tore away to tumble down the canyon, scattering sand and flaking rock from their roots. Brush within the canyon grasped frantically at the wind as it surged past but in the wind there was no purchase for thorn and bramble. Animals huddled lower where they lay, and eyes were closed against the stinging sand as legs were drawn in tighter. Spider webs vanished, nests of smaller birds became windborne, scattering egg yolk across the rocks below. There were teeth in the wind and an appetite. A lizard late in finding shelter was scooped up and it suffocated as it was hurled down the canyon like shrapnel. It was unable to pump its lungs against the pressure of the accelerating air mass and the last breath it had taken before being swept away fouled, until there was no more oxygen left to feed its hungry blood.

On the ridge the condor pushed into an opening barely big enough to receive him. He went in head first and closed his eyes against the biting particles of sand that whirled around him in a stinging spray. Fingers of wind, outriders of the giant thrust that roared past his small hiding place, swirled in at him and forced grit up under his feathers although they were tight against his body. He clucked in anger and regurgitated his interrupted meal against the rock to which he was pressed.

It was two hours before the plateau had emptied itself of excess pressure. Finally a few dust devils sprang to life, understatements in the denouement as they had been in the storm's prelude. The number of small lives that had been lost could not be reckoned, for there is no census of spider and mite, of bug and worm. Such creatures die unheralded, as they are born and as they live. Nature has created no mourners for them.

The condor backed out of his hole and shook violently. He was discolored by the dust that had settled on him and the sand that had been driven up under his feathers. He shook again and looked around. A bush here was missing, a small slide had altered the appearance of a ledge there, but no appreciable change had been made in the area. The winds had come and gone, as they always had, profitless although violent, a seemingly foolish expenditure of energy. The most significant thing about them must be a negative observation. Once again they had failed to take a condor life. Long ago the strain of condor behavior that did not heed the early warnings had been weeded out, left rotting in broken condor bodies on distant valley floors. Only those condors capable of detecting and reacting to violent weather well in advance had survived to feed the present condor form with their safer genes.

The natural things that happen in a primeval world are seldom noticeable for long. The place itself is the product of such events and alterations made are natural and quickly invisible. The world into which the condor emerged to shake the dust from his back was not really changed at all. As for the creatures that had died, the soil needed their chemicals anyway. It didn't matter, because a thousand times a million years ago Nature had known the winds would come and had fixed the reproductive rates of her species to tolerate the attrition which was thus permissible.

The wind finally eddied away into oblivion shortly before dusk began closing the valley in and the condor did not seek another meal that day. He did manage, though, to locate a small pool on a rocky knoll that rose up from the valley floor and there he bathed and drank. Several other condors promenaded around the water hole, hissing and worrying about each other. The storm had left them keyed up and their small hostile displays gave them an opportunity to siphon off some of the energy that had accumulated. When a condor couldn't find another of his kind to intimidate, he took it out on the bits and pieces of vegetable matter that the wind had left stranded as its velocity dropped. The canyon was littered with pollen, seeds, leaves, insect carcasses and other lesser flotsam from as far away as a hundred and fifty miles. Spiders that had survived the aerial roller coaster had already set about housekeeping. Several had already begun new webs, while others were still floating at twenty thousand feet, waiting for a hole in the wind that would allow their return to earth.

The condor hissed as he was hissed at and finally got away from the water hole without serious incident. He found a stark dead oak that had survived the winds, although the angle at which it now jutted out over the canyon was somewhat less than encouraging. He settled down immediately because night was closing in rapidly and he was later than usual at his perch.

Although the condor was strictly a creature of the daylight hours, much of what was important to him happened at night. It was after dark that the big predators were abroad, killing and scattering across the countryside carcasses on which the condor could later feed, and it was at night that the greatest mayhem occurred along the highways. Each morning was more than the beginning of a new day, it was a whole new treasure hunt.

While the condor slept in the hours after the Santa Ana winds had passed, the night hunters moved abroad. The tension they too had felt died down within them and they sought to satisfy the hunger each night was guaranteed to bring them. The single female puma that had moved into the valley several weeks before was hungry, for she had two unsuccessful nights of hunting behind her. Her old range to the north was hunted out and she had moved south, bringing with her old habits. In wilder times, in wilder places she would have hunted around the clock if she was really hungry but in her old range she had adjusted herself to strictly nocturnal habits. It had been too near operating ranchland and too often the sons of the ranch owners walked through her range with rifles and shotguns. Twice she had seen coyotes shot, while watching from her hidden perch, and once she had seen an ancient bobcat blown screaming out of a tree with a load of buckshot. It had been several years since she had allowed herself the luxury of a daytime hunt.

Whether it was due to her particularly demanding hunger or because the tension that had come and gone with the winds had changed her behavior patterns is hard to tell, but that night the hundred-and-twenty-five-pound puma moved down toward cultivated land. It was something she hadn't done in over seven years. She stood at the edge of a small rock jumble, where retreat could be quick and effective, while she sorted out the night. A pasture ran up almost to the spot where she stood and the ground around her reeked with cattle smells. She hung back for several minutes, revealing her uncertainty and her dread of anything human. Then, as the moon eased in behind a cloud and the pasture fell under a black shadow, she moved out along the edge of the flat and headed north. There were no cows or bulls near at hand but fifty yards in from the wire fence that picked up where the rocks left off, a mare lay on her side, breathing evenly and deeply. Near her, a colt lay asleep, his legs moving from time to time as he worked his way through whatever dreams a young horse can have.

The mare, although a seasoned veteran of open range living, was careless this one time and wasn't aware of trouble until the cat had located her, judged the wind, and begun her stalk. By the time the mare came snorting and nickering to her feet, a shadow nearby exploded into the form of a lunging cat and the colt was cut down before he could get his four feet under him. The cat hung to the back of the colt's neck, twisting and tugging, while the mare gathered her senses. The colt's struggles were soon over but the mare pressed in, exhaling violently and flailing out with her forefeet. Certain that the colt was dead, the puma released her vise grip on his neck and began circling the mare, who snorted and wheezed and sought a target for the cutting edges of her hooves. Time after time they bit into the soft loam as the cat feinted and dissolved, feinted and dissolved. Ghostlike, she drew the mare's attack and then vanished into the shadows. The mare kept up the pounding and the thrusting until she was doing it by reflex, almost as if she were in a trance. She no longer understood what she was doing or why she was doing it. It was then that the cat struck. She smashed the mare with her full weight, the impact on the wildly dancing animal sending her over onto her side. The mare was open to the bone from her shoulder to her hip. As she fought to right herself, the puma duplicated the attack she had made on the colt. The mare's head tipped forward as the puma's canine found her spine and crushed the fifth vertebra down from her skull. The mare wheezed once and the puma lowered the lolling head to the ground. She sniffed the mare and then walked over to the colt. She pawed at him, half turning him over, and then walked around to where she could open his belly. She began to feed less than twenty minutes after she had first appeared at the pasture's edge and sensed her prey asleep on the ground.

None of this the condor heard or saw and it wasn't until late the following morning that his soaring flight brought him out over the pasture at an altitude of five hundred feet and at a speed of fifty miles an hour. He saw the mare and the colt lying about ten yards apart and immediately gained altitude. At a thousand feet he circled the area four times and then angled off toward a high rock at the back of the jumble that had been the avenue of the puma's original approach. From his perch on the rock the condor watched the field for several minutes, until satisfied that it was safe for him to land. There were no coyotes in sight and the two turkey vultures and half a dozen ravens already at work on the carcass offered neither threat nor competition. They would scatter at his approach.

Kicking free of his perch, he coasted down the curve of the hill and broke his flight several feet short of the carcasses. With his wings outstretched and waddling like a shrouded goose, he moved forward. The vultures hissed and backed away, the ravens lifted off to circle overhead. When the condor settled down to feed on the mare, the other birds congregated at the body of the colt. There was more than enough to go around.

The turkey vultures and the ravens had not been the first to come upon the puma's victims. By eight o'clock that morning they had been missed at the watering trough and a rider had crisscrossed the field in search of them. He stood up in his stirrups and stared down at the carnage that littered the area, whistled softly to himself as he saw the pug marks of the puma, and rode back to the barn at full gallop.

When the two riders rode back out to the carcasses, the second man, the shorter, older one, carried a flask marked "1080," the simple cryptic designation for sodium fluoroacetate. Developed during World War II, this powerful poison is now used around the world and, although it is slower than the time-honored strychnine, it is no less deadly to most of the earth's creatures. They soaked both carcasses with the tasteless, odorless water solution and rode back to the ranch, secretly praying that the puma would come again to feed on the carcasses after nightfall.

The condor swallowed several large hunks of meat that he tore loose from the mare's carcass before the coyote appeared by the first fence post east of the rock jumble. At the sight of him, the partially glutted bird began running and hopping across the flat pastureland, until a convenient draft slipped under him and helped him clear the ground. He circled twice before leveling off at two thousand feet and disappearing over the ridge.

The coyote whose appearance drove the condor off the mare would not live to see another day. The turkey vultures who had all but eaten their fill before the condor arrived, although far more resistant to the poison than members of the dog family, would also die as a result of the meal. Even the ravens would be dead before midnight. The condor, although remarkably resistant to most of the poisons used by man in predator control, has a limited tolerance for 1080. Had the young bird eaten to his normal capacity, he would probably have perished as well. As it was, the coyote saved his life.

Shortly after reaching a perch in midafternoon, the condor began to feel the poison's effects. He regurgitated his meal and sat down deep on his perch, sensing but not understanding the fight his body was putting up to ward off the deadly effects of the sodium compound. It was an internal battle, a battle of chemicals, and although he suffered through the night, he survived. The next morning he managed to make it across the canyon to a narrow ledge and there he remained, in the shelter of a rock overhang, for two more days and nights. He was weak and sick and never very far from death. But he did live, the survivor of another condor experience in the world of men. His experience was insidious in yet another way. There was nothing he could learn from it. He would still depend on carrion every day of his life and would never have the wit to detect a baited carcass from a safe one. His ability to survive man's vengeful poison would be his ability to call on luck and nothing else.

Chapter Eleven

A STRAY BREEZE BRUSHED the chaparral gently and moved on out of the canyon. It was late in the morning and the buteos, a golden eagle, several smaller falcons and a half-dozen turkey vultures had all come and gone, some rewarded with a meal, others still hunting in the increasing heat of the near midday sun. The condor sulked on a ledge, watching and waiting. He had survived the effects of 1080 without permanent injury but he was slow in returning to a normal routine. He often sat on flat rock ledges for hours at a time when he would normally have been aloft. His temporary reluctance to fly, however, was a passing thing and each day saw him soar higher and travel further from his nighttime perch.

Another random current of air drifted past his ledge and he braced himself and then kicked free. He dropped briefly, then caught an upswing and passed over the canyon wall. At four thousand feet he leveled off and headed north. Ten miles from his ledge he dropped down again and leveled off at five hundred feet. He began scanning the broken ground below in earnest. It was time for him to feed.

The vegetation throughout the region was dry and brittle, for it had been some months since any rain had fallen. The moisture-laden clouds that had been carried through the region by winds from the sea had passed without releasing their treasure, and the ground was parched, thirsty, and dangerously ready for a spark that could ignite the jumbled brush whose roots were finding little of value as they probed into the dry dust. The pools and streams that nestled in the high valleys all around were drying up and successive irregular bands showed where the water level had dropped day by day over the weeks that had passed since they had been refreshed from above.

The condor moved over the plateau at a speed of fifty miles an hour. Ahead, on the ground near a dry bush, he saw a form that interested him. A black-tailed jackrabbit had died there the night before, the victim of mischance. He had hopped near a bush a quarter of a mile away, where a young rattlesnake had been lurking since dusk. The snake, just slightly over two feet long, had struck almost by reflex and the jackrabbit had reeled away, sickened by the venom, his body already undergoing a form of digestion by the enzymes the rattlesnake had injected. The rattlesnake began scenting along the weaving course of the dying lagomorph, although he was too small to swallow the victim he had selected. Before he could locate the jack, *Bubo*, the great horned owl, had dropped from a tree branch and, after sparring briefly, had ended the snake's life by crushing its head in the powerful beak designed for just such work. The jack had died unseen beside the bush, its hind legs kicking spastically even after the death glaze had frozen across its eyes.

The condor shrugged his shoulders, reducing his wing area to lose altitude. He swept low over the jack and curved upward to land on the same tree branch where *Bubo* had lurked before taking the rattlesnake. He watched for several minutes, until satisfied that it was safe to approach the prize, dropped off onto a passing breeze, and swung down toward the flat area near the bush. He cupped his wings, using them as brakes as he lowered and spread his tail. His legs absorbed the shock of impact and he waddled toward the jack with his wings slowly lowering. He held his prize in place with one foot while opening its lean muscular abdomen with his beak. It was not as welcome fare as a hoofed animal would have been but it was acceptable.

He was no more than half through his meal when an irregular noise from the north disturbed him and sent him hissing off the carcass, ready for instant flight. The single-engine plane was only a thousand feet above the plateau and was losing altitude rapidly. In the cockpit the pilot, facing his first real emergency, was on the verge of panic. He was losing power and it was only a matter of seconds, or minutes at best, before his engine would quit altogether. He was searching desperately for a place to set the crippled plane down but there was no suitable area in sight. The teen-age girl sitting next to him was frozen by terror and was mumbling incoherently about being good and never disobeying her parents again. But on this day there was no one who cared to listen.

The unskilled pilot had not studied his maps carefully enough. If he had cleared the western ridge of the valley into which his improperly maintained plane had dropped, he would have reached a meadow beyond and would have survived. In his ignorance he tried for the eastern ridge, which led to endless miles of tortuously broken ground. He pulled back as hard as he could but the plane didn't have the altitude. A broken blade of rock along the ridge ripped the fixed landing gear off the plane as it passed and the pilot felt himself nose over into the ravine. His left wing lodged in a Fremont cottonwood and the plane hit the slope opposite nose on. The girl screamed once as her seat tore loose, sending her forward through the windshield. There was a two-beat pause and then a black finger of smoke rose straight up in the windless draw. Gasoline from the ruptured tanks began soaking the ground and then the small sliver of fire found its mark. There was a muffled explosion, and a ball of orange flame billowed upward, decorated about its edges with black, sooty smoke. The pilot, jammed under the control panel by the impact, and the young girl, her body half in the cockpit and half sprawled grotesquely across the engine cover, were consumed in the first two minutes.

The gasoline fire spread rapidly. Burning debris had been flung in all directions by the explosion and nearly thirty smaller fires started over an area of half an acre. Each one found its own avenue and within half an hour the entire valley was engulfed. At the southern and northern ends the spreading flames found more tinder-dry vegetation and within the next two hours four adjacent valleys were in flame.

The heat from the fires started its own wind system and the flames were fanned by the energy they had unleashed.

A San Francisco-bound Navy jet was the first aircraft over the scene and the pilot radioed ahead to report the fire. A hurried phone call was put through to Fire Control of the U.S. Forest Service and a standby helicopter took off to locate the fix the Navy pilot had provided. Circling the area, the helicopter pilot and observer were unable to spot the plane wreck because of the dense smoke and it was thought that the blaze had been caused by lightning, or so the first tentative report read. Within minutes after radioing the alarming extent of the blaze, the helicopter was joined by two other observation craft. Parachute-equipped fire fighters were enplaning to the south, and tanker bombers were being readied for flight to the north. All of man's available technology was being rapidly aligned to battle one of the most primeval forces on earth. But much damage had already been done.

The screeching impact of the landing gear against the knife-edge ridge had sent the condor flapping desperately across the plateau. By the time the plane had crashed beyond the ridge, the condor was airborne. He was several hundred feet up before the explosion took place. He gained altitude rapidly and curved away from the valley that was now in flames.

Then, strangely, he circled back. His curiosity, something a condor never seems quite able to control, required one final check of the area. Something unusual had happened within his range and he had to know what it was. He wasn't long in coming upon the rising billows of heated air, and the smell of the oily smoke was harsh and dangerously unfamiliar. He banked through a cloud of drifting smoke already made gray by dilution and rose sharply. He reached six thousand feet and headed south at sixty miles an hour.

The wind rose that afternoon and by the time the parachutists were over the area, the flames were spreading rapidly into several new canyons. The brush-choked floors of the parched draws were ideal fodder for the greedy flames and a full-scale brush fire racing insanely out of control was in the offing. The parachutists dropped down through the black smoke and within minutes of their hazardous landings were at work, cutting avenues through the brush in an effort to contain the flames within the areas already ignited. Thousands of small animals were driven before the flames and the fire fighters were constantly endangered by rattlesnakes angered by the disturbance and made frantic by the increasing heat at their backs. They slithered forward, flopping off rocks and pushing through the very brush the men were trying to cut back. One man was bitten on the thigh as he passed too close to a rocky prominence and a helicopter made the hazardous descent to get him out. Seven tanker bombers flew back and forth over the valleys that were already in flames, dumping hundreds of thousands of gallons of borate on the creeping fire. Time and again they returned to their base to reload.

The wind died down toward nightfall but when the long, dark shadows fell across the land, seven square miles of brush glowed a brilliant orangy-red. It was still a fire out of control and the men, bolstered by reserve forces, continued their fight until dawn, when the winds rose again. Flaming debris leaped the gaps and new fires began cropping up in several areas. The men who had fought during the darkness were finally relieved and new forces were moved in overland and in new air drops. Tens of thousands of gallons of borate were added to the loads already deposited by the tankers and slowly the advance of the flames was arrested. The sun shone a dull orange in a sky badly stained by smoke and floating soot. The acrid stench drifted over an area of more than two hundred square miles and newspapers as far away as New York carried reports that the condor sanctuary was in danger. Phone calls flew back and forth between New York and Washington, between both cities and Fire Control in Fillmore. Two biologists left Los Angeles by car with instructions to report their findings by radio as soon as they could work their way into the area.

Three human lives were lost in the catastrophe, the pilot, his young companion and a fire fighter whose parachute failed to open. Tens of thousands of small animals and a dozen mule deer also perished. The condors, because they could escape the fire in high-altitude flight and because the men who were thrown into the battle were able to bring the inferno under control before it reached their restricted nesting area, survived, all but one. A helicopter, in assessing the extent of the fire's threat, had swept by an exposed ridge in which a single condor nest was located. As it passed, two adult condors were caught by the shattering noise while in the act of feeding their nestling. They scrambled out onto the ledge and dropped off in wild confusion. They swept away with the wind, never to return. The nestling was dead of starvation a few days later. Instead of eight new condors being added to the world's population of forty-three that year there would be seven. Unfortunately eight condors would die from a variety of causes and the species slipped one giant step closer to total extinction.

Chapter Twelve

THE CONDOR'S APPEARANCE had been changing nearly every day of his life and would continue to do so until he was at least five years old and in full adult regalia. These changes, though, had been discreet and slow and not at all obvious. A condor molts slowly, irregularly, and therefore never emerges dramatically from a cave one day, freshly laundered and newly feathered. It probably takes a condor two full years to complete a molt and except in the month of December, when all members of the species seem to be intact, a condor is more apt to look ragged than not.

At three and a half, the young male was progressing well into his subadult phase of development. He was no longer properly considered a juvenile although he still had some genuinely juvenile characteristics. His head had a small scattering of gray feathers, giving him a sooty appearance, and his neck was still gray except for a narrow band of pink skin that was nearly hidden by his highly mobile neck ruff. In the months ahead, that pink ring would expand upward until it reached his head. By that time, his head would be a shocking orange.

It was no longer possible to tell the color of his eyes. They had been brown and would one day be red. At three and a half they were both, depending on which light you saw him in. He was a bird in transition, and this, too, was dictated by gene patterns. They knew where they were going and what they were doing in the creation of the best of all possible condors, as Evolution had defined it.

As a subadult the young male was about the same size as his parents. He weighed twenty-one and a half pounds and had a wingspan of just over nine feet. He was about average.

One aspect of his appearance remained a source of peril for him. He did not yet have the stark-white triangular underwing markings of the adult. When seen from most angles, his underwing area appeared uniform and he was easily mistaken for a turkey vulture, although he was larger, or a golden eagle, although he did not have prominent white marking on the underside of his similarly fan-shaped tail. To those who were inclined to make such a mistake, the opportunity was there.

It is impossible to estimate the number of individual notifications that have been issued to the residents of the southern half of California asking them to avoid causing injury to large, dark soaring birds. The condor's aerial partners are all worthy of protection, although none are in such dire peril as he. The rare bald eagle, the occasional golden eagle, the turkey vultures, although plentiful, the smaller Cooper hawk, the distinctly lighter sharp-shinned hawk and goshawks, the very different red-tailed, Swainson's and marsh hawks, all should be able to live out their well-balanced lives without disturbance, but such is not the case. Shotguns and well-scoped rifles are turned in their direction at every opportunity and the only defense the condor has is to grow up, develop his sharply delineated underwing markings, and make the mistake less likely to occur. There are, of course, an inevitable number of people who will shoot a condor fully knowing what he is, but they are relatively few. Still, the tens of thousands of leaflets, the endless magazine and newspaper articles, the lectures, speeches and vows, offered, given and taken at Boy Scout, 4-H and Grange meetings have not yet been enough. It is hardly possible to credit the idea that anyone in the small region where the condor still exists could be ignorant of the facts, but such is the case.

For almost two weeks the young male had been working his way back and forth over the burned-out area during available daylight hours. Several of the deer, two feral horses and a multitude of the small creatures that had perished in the flames were in areas suitable for a condor's dining. Nearly half of the remaining California condors in the world had the same idea and a number of other birds given to living on carrion followed the pattern. The result was a greater concentration of large birds than was likely in a similar area anywhere else in the state. As long as the sun was in the sky there was a steady coming and going of great winged creatures, sailing in over the charred ridges to land on the new moonscape amid a rising of dust and a hissing of fellow scavengers. Six and seven condors could be seen at a time, feeding on a single deer carcass, and others would be nearby waiting their turn. Even as life began its march back through the disaster area, the condors and other collectors were busy cleaning up the last vestiges of that which had gone before and had died in the flames.

The brush fire, particularly when it was established that a fatal plane wreck had been the cause, attracted a lot of attention. Once the fire was out and the area was opened again, lines of cars snaked along the few roads in the region, bringing the morbid and the just plain curious. Private planes circled the area at dangerously low altitudes as weekend pilots brought their friends out for a quick survey of the burned-over area and, as the *pièce de résistance*, a low-level pass over the wrecked plane that had been the cause of it all. Of course, little of it was recognizable, but it was still possible to look down at the charred pieces of steel and think of it as the violent tomb of two young people. Being in a light plane looking down at where a light plane had died gave many people a distinctively superior feeling. Ironically, one plane lost power and barely made it back to a meadow twenty miles away and two other light planes very nearly collided over the scene of the crash.

One of the automobiles that made its way into the area as part of a chain of flivvers, wrecks and heaps contained four young men, two in their twenties, two hanging precariously onto the last few months of their teens. Not one of the young men had ever hunted a dangerous game animal, not one had ever earned a trophy. None of them knew how to track, how to stalk, or even how to care for their guns properly. They had never reloaded their own shells, they knew nothing of ballistics, had never hired a guide, and were uniformly no better than average shots. Yet, the four considered themselves hunters, even sportsmen, if you will. They had neither the skill of hunters nor the traditions nor the sense of responsibility of sportsmen. They were hacks ahunting, slaughterers, killers who drank cases of beer afield, and who never measured an animal taken or reported a finding to parties interested. If they shot a banded duck the band went out with the entrails. Yet they had the killer's instinct, each of them, and they saw the unusual number of soaring birds overhead as they wound down a secondary road admiring the scorched and saddened world around them. And, as vowed, two days later they were back, guns and beer in hand.

The condor swept in over the ridge behind the four young men and banked away at the sight of them to spiral upward.

Their backs were to him and he wasn't seen. By turning in tight circles and soaring on fixed wings that had to make only the finest of adjustments, he was able to keep them in sight for several minutes before being seen. Finally, wearied by their four-mile hike over broken ground in temperatures that nudged upward toward 102 degrees, the four killers settled onto a flat rock and opened the insulated case two of them had struggled ludicrously with throughout their climb. The church key was located and the beer frothed out to their sighs of satisfaction.

One of the men, the oldest, proudly sported several finely barred amber-brown feathers that less than an hour earlier had been part of the flight mechanism of a handsome hawk as it coursed across the canyon calling *kreeeer* to the world below. The feathers, now hanging from the *sportsman's* belt were stale and foolish, for they no longer had a function. They were all that had been claimed from the hawk after it had plunged earthward in a broken heap in answer to the bullet that had gone up to meet it at twenty-six hundred feet a second. A badly worn boot with heavily ridged rubber soles had pinned the carcass to the dry earth as a calloused hand roughly tore the feathers loose. It had been an insult to life, a curse in concrete form, a profanity and a waste, but it was called *hunting* by its practitioners.

The condor had been over another valley a dozen miles away when the hawk was snuffed out of existence and didn't know the threat that was offered. He caught an updraft and soared to two thousand feet as his circling flight brought him within the men's peripheral vision. They saw him, lowered their cans of beer, and stared in quiet reptilian fascination. Here was another living thing, and *a big 'un.*

Even though stupefied by beer and their power of

death, the men had to watch for a minute, for the young condor's flight was magnificent against the clear, absolutely featureless blue sky. Without moving his wings he cut and dropped, rose and soared. Figure eights, reversals of direction, up, down, it was all accomplished with imperceptible shoulder shrugs and minute adjustments of primaries and rectrices. The young bird's flight of curiosity brought him dangerously close several times, but before a gun could be leveled he swept away, only to approach again.

In all fairness, the men did not know he was a subadult California condor. To them he was just another *buzzard*, although it is not at all clear that they would have acted any differently if they had had his scientific name tattooed on their forearms. They were out for a day of fun, and fun to them meant broken carcasses. The bigger the carcasses the more masculine and justified they became. It was, after all, a ritual and nothing more. In their culture no one had dignified their action by giving it religious or political status but it was the same as the Masai youth going against the lion with a spear and zebra-skin shield, although, of course, the condor was a whit less threatening, except insofar as it was alive and different.

Several times the condor was on the verge of sweeping away with the wind, but he had fed and he had bathed and really had nothing better to do than examine any strange phenomena within his range. And, too, there were the beer cans that were scattered about on the sand near the rock. The sun reflecting off their shiny ends flashed and twinkled and they were objects worth being curious about. And so the condor circled in again, ignoring the black stick that aimed skyward and traced his course. The cross hairs in the 4X scope moved up from his tail to his abdomen, across his chest and out past his head. When the converging lines led him by what the beer-sodden and ever brave hunter was sure was just the right amount, the black stick spoke and the condor stuttered in his flight. The shock of the impact carried through the length of his body and, for an instant, the bird that carried the history of his planet in his blood was in danger of falling from the sky. The bullet passed through a fleshy area on his belly but miraculously missed all vital organs. A few inches one way would have seen the bullet smash through his liver and his life would have ended. A few inches the other way would have carried the projectile into and through the ridge on his sternum, the anchor point of his mighty wing muscles, with the same final result. But it was a fortunate shot, if there can be such a thing. The bullet was still flying straight and had not yet begun to keyhole. The punctures were clean and the condor, recovering from the initial shock wave, swung away. Three other guns were snapped off but the bullets spun wild, and the condor was gone, amid curses and war whoops.

He landed ten miles away, in a tall tree in a sheltered valley. He regurgitated his still undigested meal and shook. The bleeding had stopped although at first it had looked as if it would be profound. He was stiff and the two holes in his flesh pained him with fingers of fire. He shook again and tried to regurgitate a second time but there was nothing to rid himself of. He raised his rump and ejected a horizontal stream of cream-colored excrement. He shook again and tried to settle down on his perch. Several times he attempted to adjust his position and pecked quizzically at the two wounds on his underside. The pain was increasing as the shock wore off and he finally kicked free and coasted across to a flat shelf on the cliff wall. Here, too, he tried to accommodate his posture to his pain, but there were no comfortable positions. He finally surrendered to it and, after another exploratory peck, huddled down and suffered as his eyes closed. Once again he was a very sick condor, and once again he had learned a useless lesson: that the company of men meant pain and, inevitably, death. However, just as he would still be unable to avoid a baited carcass, though he be sickened by a dozen, he would still not know enough to avoid the men he so often saw below. Nature, somehow, had failed to see this special need in planning the condor design. She had left out that extra bit of intelligence that was now wanting so badly. Unhappily, there are too few condors left now, with too little time left to them, and the design will never be improved, not with so pitifully few genes left in the pool to draw upon.

Chapter Thirteen

THE CONDOR'S WOUND was slow to repair. Movement, any movement at all, caused a searing pain and he quickly learned to remain still for hours, squatting down with his eyes closed. He could have easily been mistaken for a dead bird. His feathers remained unpreened and his head seemed to loll forward. Without animation he hardly seemed a condor at all.

The greatest danger to the condor was not the extent of the wound itself, for it was essentially superficial, but the resultant immobility. He was slowly starving, for the pain that was always present robbed him of his confidence. He was afraid to fly and his food sources remained scattered over dozens of square miles, where only confident flight could take him.

Finally, though, his hunger was too much for him and he took a few tentative steps toward the edge of the shelf. It was the sixth day after he had been shot and the pain had lessened considerably. A good wind was blowing down the canyon and, after hesitating for a few minutes, he swept free and drifted away until he came to a broad flat where the canyon spilled out onto lower ground. There was a stream nearby and he landed near a brush tangle where he had spotted a ground squirrel. It was one of several that had been killed the day before by a feral house cat who lived back in the canyon and who was in the habit of killing much more than she could possibly use as food. It was a recreation with her, a distorted instinct that had lingered on in her domestic strain for hundreds of generations, only to return as a perversion when it was summoned up by necessity.

He felt a wave of sickening pain sweep through him as his legs took the shock of impact and he stood where he landed for several minutes before approaching the carcass. But he was hungry and did finally move forward to his meal. He was weakened by his hunger and his pain and it was fortunate that he was able to finish without being disturbed. He rose briefly into the air and, after flying a hundred feet, landed near a pool that a slowly running stream left cradled in a jumble of partially eroded rock. He bathed and sunned himself although he still felt pain when his movements were abrupt. He finally lifted free of the area and returned to the shelf to which he had gone immediately following his misadventure with the *sportsmen.*

It was two more days before he left the shelf again, to feed on a jackrabbit carcass near a secondary road that led into an adjacent canyon. And so, by carefully rationing his energy, he managed to survive his wound to emerge twenty days after the incident fairly intact. He had come a great deal closer to losing his life than his limited intelligence would ever be able to comprehend. Mankind, the desire to kill that which could not be consumed, firearms, all the ingredients of the play in which he had been an unwilling participant were concepts that he could never understand. He had no more knowledge or understanding of what had happened to him than the brush that had been consumed in the fire. Just as it had been with the poisoning, it was something that had happened, had sickened him, but was not readily associated with any situation that could be grasped and avoided in the future.

Within three weeks of the shooting, the condor

was again surveying vast land areas spreading out from the high rock tangles of the Topatopa Mountains. Although he was still the victim of occasional stabs of pain, they did not reflect in his skill aloft and it was not possible to tell that this was a bird recently in communion with death.

The weight he had lost returned quickly as his general tone and mobility improved. His gluttonous appetite and the aggressiveness that went with it returned as well and he continued his march toward maturity, utilizing all of his condor gifts, all of his condor elements, as he pushed forward toward the day when he could repay the cosmos for the loan of his chemicals by reproducing himself in kind.

Of all the food eaten by the condor today, and there are at least two dozen species of animal known to be on the list, the deer and the calf are the most highly preferred. A deer carcass, and the rare calf that becomes available, will draw up to half the world's California condor population. Their enthusiasm at such feeding sites is greater than at any other time and here social dominance is most clearly demonstrated.

The condor saw three others of his kind circling like the legions of Malphas over a region of interest. Interpreting their flight as a survey pattern, he banked toward them, rose up with a lifting current, and came in over them in a fixed-wing sweep. Noting their objective, he slowly moved down to their level and took up his position in the spiral. One by one they dropped. Hunching and shrugging, they broke their flight and positioned themselves in trees and on ledges, surrounding the small plateau with the deer carcass on its westward-facing slope. Two birds were already on the carcass and in their turn the observers kicked loose from their perches and moved onto the meal. As the number of condors on the ground increased, the survey time was shortened for each arriving bird. The last to arrive landed directly on the slope, eliminating the precautionary stop on the way. The congregation gave confidence to the last to arrive.

There were thirteen birds on the deer at one time. They shouldered one another aside, hissed, argued, tugged, and evacuated in the excitement of the black mass. The abdomen was opened and all the viscera except the stomach and intestines devoured. The legs were stripped down to the hooves and the muzzle and jaws picked clean. One particularly large male got his head stuck in between two of the deer's ribs. There was a brief flurry of excitement at the carcass until the struggling bird managed to pull himself loose and stagger away, hissing violently at the other birds who shouldered in, trying to take his place. In the tugging and pulling, the carcass was moved nearly forty yards down the slope. It began to come apart as it was skeletonized and the area was littered. The grass around was crushed flat and condor feathers, condor droppings and deer offal were spread over nearly a quarter of an acre. The young male was tugging at the remains of the deer's head when it came loose and he dragged it off about a dozen feet and stood over it with his shroudlike wings spread wide, hissing furiously at two younger birds who tried to close in on his prize. The deer's unwanted intestines were strung out and draped over a bush in an obscene display. Overhead, turkey vultures circled in tight spirals, waiting their turn. Ravens, black and harshly vocal, were settled on all available perches surrounding the area, calling for the condors to be done. It was an impatient and untidy day in Gehenna.

Those condors who had eaten their fill waddled off a short distance and stood around, blinking, watching the show. There was a kind of mad carnival atmosphere to the scene and some of the birds hung on as spectators for an hour and more after finishing their own meal. The deer that had died in the sun had an aroma distinctly appropriate to the situation and the effluvium of death arose from the scattered offal. Several ravens had gotten to the carcass before the condors arrived and the deer's eyes had been the first things to go. The detached head which the young male had dragged away stared with hollow sockets at the bird who would eat the brains that once had coordinated the beautiful swift life of the mule deer buck.

The scene was not a pretty one, for death had happened here and there is an aroma to death and a pervasive sense of it as well. But then, the autopsy room of a hospital and the embalming room of a funeral parlor are not pretty places either. Nature, in planning life, had to plan death and that is why she created the condor out of earlier feathered ideas. Someone, something, has to do the work they do, for they are an agency of conversion in a natural economy where everything that existed is ultimately converted and nothing is lost. In a matter of hours they had taken a reeking, bloated carcass that was nothing more than a useless bag of rapidly spoiling chemicals and returned these chemicals to a task suited to their original purpose, the supporting of life. The terrible suffocating stink of the dead animal was less now and would quickly melt away. What they left of the great deer carcass was broken apart and scattered and made immediately available to the smaller sweepers in the scheme, who would quickly reduce it further. The condors, and those who did the same kind of work, had the power to take death and return it to life. They were an agency of the immortality of life.

Through them there was transmigration. What,

then, was ugly on the surface was really a thing of beauty, for if any life that has been created as a part of the scheme and whose task is the sustaining and carrying forward of that scheme is not beautiful, then no life is. No man has the wisdom to separate one life from another and state that one belongs while the other is alien. Nothing can be alien or everything is. The scheme is a complete thing, a total picture of the biology of the one planet we know anything about, and no one has the power or the right to dissect it and judge its parts. Whether student, casual observer or philosopher, we can only see it one way, *in toto*, for life, like Enoch, will be there at the end of time. The vanity that would declare otherwise is too gross, too perverted for us to really comprehend.

The fuss the condors made at the carcass and the smells that the winds carried away attracted other creatures who were also interested in such matters. Two coyotes worked their way up from the south end of the canyon and a third crossed over a break in the ridge from the east. In time they revealed themselves to the condors, who rose away from the scene and circled in silhouette against the brilliant, hot sky. They strung off from their circular tracks and came to rest near water holes spread over an area of a dozen miles. A condor may live on the dead but he doesn't like smelling like death or having the remnants of his meal upon his feathers. Assiduously, each condor washed away the gore, the dust and the smell of the business their way of life had forced upon them. Feathers were preened and each bird then found a high platform, where his widespread wings and exposed body could be dried in the sun. It was late afternoon before the water holes were abandoned and the birds settled on their private roosts. In a very clean, very efficient and very natural way Nature's will had been done. The landscape was better for the condors' work and their lives were sustained. And there would be more work to do the next day, and every day thereafter, for life is a constant in the biological community, and death is as well.

Chapter Fourteen

THE MALE WAS APPROACHING his maturity. He was no longer a subadult, really, but a young adult about to blossom. In the course of his five years of life within the restricted condor community he had encountered on the ground, on perches, or in the air, every other free-living specimen of his species not once but, in most cases, dozens of times. There were condors who would forever be dominant over him and there were others for whom his increasing boldness was a disruptive force, moving them further down the ladder of condor society.

As his self-assurance increased, he expressed it more and more in the pattern of chasing. Occasionally he would drive another condor off a perch, not because he wanted or needed the perch for himself but because it fulfilled something within him to prevail in an encounter. At first, the birds he chose to challenge were birds of his own year or younger but as time passed he began seeking issue with older birds, many of whom had already bred. There was no physical damage done in these episodes, indeed there was virtually never any contact, but it was a display of might and he found it satisfying and fulfilling.

On one occasion he soared in over a ridge and saw below him a large male, a very old bird, that he knew from previous encounters. It was a bird who had bullied him on many a carcass and had driven him completely off a potential meal on a number of occasions. Several times he had been forced to wait, hissing and grunting on the sidelines with the turkey vultures, until the male had eaten his fill. He recognized the big bird and dipped hesitantly once, watching the dark form plane away at a lower altitude.

But then something happened. Without really understanding what he was doing or why he was doing it, the young male broke into a rapid flex-glide. Although the tips of his primary feathers remained turned up, he flexed his wrists to the point where the actual ends of his wings themselves were on a level with his breast. At the same time he pulled in the edges of his tail until they were nearly parallel. The result was a drop in altitude at an angle of forty-five degrees, and a rapid increase in speed. He began closing on the old male in a plunging glide.

When he was only a half-mile off his target, the older bird sensed the beginning of the chase and flexed himself, dropping rapidly and accelerating. He twisted and turned often, banking so sharply that he was completely over on his side. He rushed toward a cliff face on what appeared to be a collision course, dropped a few more feet and then soared upward. The younger bird repeated the action exactly. The sound the wind in their feathers made at the bottom of their dive could be heard over half a mile away. It was like the roar of steam escaping, and other animals stopped to look and listen.

When he broke his dive near the bottom of the cliff, the target bird banked, rose, and sailed rapidly up the rock face. The pursuing bird did exactly the same thing. Two enormous black forms were silhouetted briefly against the pale dullness of the rock before breaking out above to sail against the blue, leaving the echoes of their rushing bodies to play out in the rocky crevasse. Their shadows scudded over the broken ground like frantic ghost animals chasing each other in a crazy tarantella. They rose and fell in their game and the shadow creatures increased and decreased in size as they hopped boulders and flew in and out of holes in the ground.

Twice more they flexed into steep, rapid dives and twice more they rose high above the valley floor, and then the big male broke and soared away at low level. They had never come close to touching each other but the younger bird had expressed his newly found dominance in the intricate social order and would never again be chased off a carcass by the older bird.

He circled twice now that he was alone and the sky and the valley were his and came down to roost on a stunted tree at the edge of the cliff. He shook himself and issued several abrupt belchlike grunts. He had begun to settle down when another form darted in over the cliff opposite and banked into a sharp curve, sharper and faster than any he could accomplish. The lightninglike movements of the peregrine falcon put him immediately on guard and as the much smaller but bolder bird closed up the tail of a tight turn he kicked free of his perch and dropped down toward the valley floor. As the peregrine dropped in pursuit, both he and his frantically scudding shadow were no more than blurs of movement. Ignominiously, the condor left the scene of his triumph, relinquishing the valley to the swifter, more aggressive pirate. The young male's dominance could extend over others of his kind and many lesser birds as well, but the falcons, like the eagles, would always be able to put him to flight. There was a position for him, one that had been designed long ago, and he would never be able to exceed it.

There are laws in California, specifically California Fish and Game Code Sections 1172 and 1179, that protect the condor from further destruction by man. The terrible slaughter that took place between 1875 and 1895 and very nearly pushed the species over the brink to extinction has all but been brought to a halt. However, there are other forces that the laws of men cannot order and shape. A few hours after the condor fled before the peregrine falcon, such forces were organizing their potential far above him, far beyond those places in the sky where even his powerful flight could take him.

High winds shunted onshore and a mass of moisture-laden air drifted in across the coast from the sea. The mass had been rolling turbulently northward from the Mexican coast for days, and fresh winds knifing over the mountains and a low-pressure area that had shifted down from the north conspired to lure the mass inland. The result was a rapid build-up of clouds high above the earth. The tops of the clouds carried a positive electric charge, while the zones closest to the earth were negative. Although no rain was reaching the earth, there was movement of both large and small water particles within the clouds themselves. The stress built within the vast static machine until it surpassed its own holding power. The first hint of lightning illuminated the interior of the gray clouds with ghost fires that crackled and reflected as their energy increased. A full-blown electric storm was gathering its determination.

Other forces were at work as well. High up where the storm was building, great vortices spun at furious speeds. Cloud-laden air rushed inward toward the center and was sent spiraling upward. The clouds thus affected carried water droplets at fairly warm temperatures but when they spun upward they were projected into zones of ever decreasing temperature. When they finally hurled out through the tops of the whirlwinds, the droplets sank slowly down the outsides of the inverted cones only to be sucked in again at the bottom and sent upward through the progressively more frigid zones again. Time after time the same water droplets were fired upward and time after time they descended. But on each trip they froze a little more solid and each time they were coated with yet another layer of ice. Soon they were the size of hazelnuts and consisted of alternating layers of clear and frosted ice. In some cases two or more globules of ice collided at the lower altitudes and froze together in lumps as they rose. Even after they achieved the status of hailstones and should have fallen free from the carnival of air, pulled down by their own weight, they continued in the cycle. The winds were too strong, the whirlpools of spinning air too persistent, and they continued to build in size.

Some of them grew to more than two inches in diameter, oblately spheroidal hunks of superfrozen ice, before their weight tore them loose from the system and let them fall. In distant valleys greenhouses were pocked, then completely destroyed, and along highways and in parking lots, automobile windshields were shattered. People ran for shelter as glass crumbled around them and the drumming of the hailstones on roofs sent children screaming in terror into the arms of their parents.

The condor, though, has no basements to which it can flee. Those that could reached caves and rocky overhangs, while others landed in places where the vegetation was thickest. With grunted complaints, they waddled like distressed black geese into the most sheltered areas. One old female, with only a few breeding seasons left to her, settled dumbly on an exposed branch and sat there, grunting and preening her feathers in displacement activity until she was beaten to death and smashed to the valley floor far below.

The young male was high above the earth when the hail began to fall. As the first missiles hurtled past him he veered, flexed, and began his descent. He had never seen hail before but instinctively recognized it as a hazard. Discerning immediately that he could not fly above its source or outrun it, he chose instead to seek whatever protection the earth could offer. The lightning had started in earnest and as he dropped, livid flashes bolted earthward. Thunderous echoes of the discharges rolled against the cliffs as he swung in at the end of a valley. At that point the first hailstone hit his left wing and sent him veering sharply to the right, dangerously close to the cliff face. Panicking under the influence of the pain that roared upward through his shoulder, he rose again instead of continuing his descent and swept across the valley into the next. The ground there was flat and had once been pastureland for a long-dead ranch. He swept low, passed some trees and, as he was about to land, encountered the dreaded vestige of man's territorialism. Both of his legs, now lowered in preparation for landing, hit the wire at the same time, but only his left leg broke. He careened to earth and crumbled on impact. Slowly, he managed to right himself as the last of the giant hailstones fell nearby, pocking into the dust, and the rain began.

The game warden had pulled his dusty jeep into a clump of trees when the hail began to fall and had finally crawled under his machine when the first holes were punctured in the canvas roof of his vehicle. When the plopping impact of the hailstones began to fade he stuck his head out to look around and saw the condor crash. For a moment he feared the giant bird had died but as he came forward toward the black mass in the feral pasture he saw the reassuring movement of life and ran back to his jeep. Rummaging around in the back he found the sheet of canvas that had so often served him as a lean-to when nightfall found him far from home. Moving cautiously, so as not to further panic the bird, he slipped from bush to bush until he was only ten feet away from where the giant lay struggling, trying hopelessly to adjust to his crippling injury. Easily sizing the situation up the ranger made the last advance and threw the canvas over the young male, who immediately settled down in the blackness that had come over him. He didn't resist when he felt the canvas being gathered gently under him and only grunted when he was lifted off the ground and carried to the jeep. As he was lowered carefully onto the right-hand seat with the canvas still surrounding him like a great, stiff ball, he vomited up the remnants of his last meal and shrugged himself lower, trying to keep his leg free of responsibility.

The care he received at the zoo was calculated to prepare him for a prompt return to the wild. He and the genes he carried were far too valuable to allow his benefactors the luxury of holding him in captivity any longer than was absolutely essential. The veterinarian came often to check his progress once the splint was removed. He was given no prepared foods or slaughterhouse meat that might affect his appetite or alter his food preferences. Dead animals were collected along the highways and thrown to him just as they had been found. His enclosure was far removed from the public viewing areas and only those people who had reason to be near him had the chance to watch him as he sat on his perch waiting for the fates to finish their little game.

The veterinarian stood off behind a small shack, watching. The keeper threw in the dead jackrabbit, a victim of a speeding car at dusk the day before. The condor eyed the offering from his perch, a dead tree with skeletal limbs attached that had been brought in to make his temporary home as natural as possible. Having reassured himself, the condor hopped down with his wings spread. The veterinarian watched with special care as the condor landed and stepped on the jackrabbit with his left leg before bending to the task of feeding. The veterinarian nodded to the warden, "He's fine, John. Turn him loose."

That night, hours after he had settled onto his perch and long after all lights in the area had been extinguished, the warden and the highly experienced keeper who had been assigned to this very special charge slipped into the wire enclosure and slowly lowered a pillowcase over the sleeping bird's head. They used two long sticks to complete the difficult maneuver without frightening him. The keeper climbed the ladder that the warden held against the tree and carefully tucked the twenty-one-pound bird under his arm. Two hours later he was on his way back to the Sespe Wildlife Area in Ventura County in a padded crate in the back of a pickup truck. Two newsmen picked by lot followed in a car with an official of the National Audubon Society. In its own way it was a very special event, for the young male condor shortly due to enter his first breeding season was one of the most valuable animals in the world. There wasn't a zoo in the world that wouldn't have paid a fortune to possess him and there wasn't a zoo in the world that could own him legally. A nation newly proud of its wildlife heritage had declared him and his kind forever inviolate.

It was dawn when the warden and the keeper carefully lowered the hinged front of the crate. The condor huddled in the corner of his den, the cotton sack still over his head. The cameras were already set up and the warden reluctantly heeded the pleas of the newsman to wait a few more minutes until the sun was a little higher in the sky. Ten minutes later they took him out of the crate and carried him to the crest of the hill. The land fell away in a gentle slope and the ground was clear for several hundred feet. The warden set the bird on his own feet, facing him down the hill. The keeper slipped the sack off his head and both men stood back. The condor that they had nicknamed Gym after his scientific name, *Gymnogyps californianus*, stood blinking in the bright morning sun that streamed in from the east. He turned, saw his captors, and eyed curiously the movie cameras perching on their triangular legs. He took a step or two, felt a ground draft, and began waddling forward at increasing speed.

After he lifted off, the condor flew in a straight line away from the hill for several miles before banking back and soaring over familiar territory. The men on the hill watched him as long as he was still a dark speck in the new morning sky and then turned back to their lives as they had been before the condor had become their partner in the quiet adventure that had just been terminated. He hadn't been their pet, not at all, nor had he been an adornment they could show off to other people. Yet, for them, there was a hollow place that he had once filled. They couldn't quite define it because it went beyond that. Perhaps it was their sense of his worth that caused it, or perhaps it was because he had been alive and they were men of special sensitivity. The written and photographic report that reached the headquarters of the National Audubon Society on Fifth Avenue in New York a few days later would be cryptic, precise, without embellishment or emotion. But the men reading it there and those reading the carbons that were circulated in Washington would understand. Somehow, each of them would quietly wish that they, too, had had a direct hand in the saving of a young male California condor.

Chaparral has great tenacity of life, wonderful recuperative powers. The smoldering ruins of the burned-out valleys, with the gray and white ash lying inches deep, had quickly repaired themselves following the plane crash and the ensuing holocaust. Once again it became an area where animals could feed themselves and reproduce themselves in kind. It was on a dead tree no more than a quarter of a mile from the spot where the plane had come to earth that the young male met the female who was to be his mate.

He settled on a perch near her and waited for a sign that didn't come. Gathering his nerve at last, he hopped up onto the branch beside her, only to be met by a peck that caught him on the back of his maturely naked neck. He retreated a few inches and waited. Finally, the female kicked free and sailed across the canyon to a high rock. The male followed. Throughout the rest of the day the male followed the female wherever she went. At times she just ignored him, while at others she hissed and even snapped at him. Still, he persisted and when she settled down that night he was no more than six feet away. The two birds looked exactly alike. Only from the fact that the one was pursuing the other could it be told which was which, or even that they were not of the same sex.

Late the following morning the female landed on a rock far up on a steeply sloping ledge. The male had been following since she left her perch shortly after eight o'clock. She turned and waited for him to land. She was resigned to what was to follow.

The male landed and walked up to within six feet of the female. They stood there facing each other for several minutes before he began his premating display. He slowly spread his wings wide, allowing the primaries at their tips to sag until they touched the ground. He extended his neck forward and downward, presenting the top of his head and the back of his neck to his partner-to-be. Inclining his body slightly forward, he allowed his tail to drag on the ground and stood there for several moments, almost rigid. Slowly, he turned to his partner's right and shuffled forward in short, abrupt steps. He returned to the position in front of her, moving his wings slightly so that the distinct white patches on their undersides flashed in the brilliant morning sun. He then shuffled to her left and again returned to her front. Back and forth he moved, his wing tips and tail feathers dragging in the dust, drawing confusing little trails. His was an intense posturing, for the purpose behind it was the most profound in the world. Back and forth, toward her and away, but always within her line of sight.

Throughout it all the female was actively disinterested. She was a study in how to be unimpressed. She did everything but yawn to show that she was bored, that she wouldn't care if he stood on his head in his excitement. This too was part of the plan, for her lack of reaction drove him to even more frenzied posturing and spastic movements. Actually, she was as excited as he was but Nature had not invited her into the display game except as an apparently disinterested member of the audience.

There were two other members of that audience. They were both immature condors, both males, and their interest was strictly academic. They strained forward to watch but knew instinctively that this was not the time to approach the area where the female was standing, not, at least, while the male was so aroused. Finally, one of the two immatures could stand it no longer and turned to the other, pecking him viciously on the side of the head. It wasn't with any purpose, and after a bit of hissing and nibbling they flopped off their ledge and sought instead a more practical outlet for their energies, a treasure of carrion that had been ripening in the sun.

At last the male reached a peak of excitement and bumped into the female with exaggerated clumsiness. She pecked at him and he retaliated by putting his foot squarely on the top of her head and pressing down. She moved away and again he bumped her. This time she moved toward him and passed under one of his extended wings. She pulled a few feathers out of his side as she passed but he didn't seem to mind.

Twice more that day he displayed for her. It was always high up on the cliff wall and always her reaction was the same, disinterest to the point of disdain until the very end, when she would pass under his wing and brush against his body.

Just before dusk they were standing together on the very edge of a cliff topping a steep wall at the north end of the valley. He moved toward her but instead of posturing he grasped her beak in his own and began moving his head back and forth. This time she didn't act disdainful and reciprocated the neck wrestling until together they lost their balance and flopped off into space.

Had they been experienced birds they would probably have mated the first or second day. As it was, they were both unlimbering newly released instincts for the first time and there was an element of delay involved. Neither bird knew what to do next but in blind, dumb faith followed the path that had long ago been defined for them. They had never watched another pair of birds display or mate, at least not while consciously knowing what was going on. This, the most critical single act either of them could ever perform, was not a matter of knowledge but of pure instinct. Since no two species of birds display in quite the same way, it was something that had been worked out long, long ago as exactly suiting the needs of the species. Perhaps the bright red eyes, perhaps the underwing white triangles, perhaps a combination of these and yet other peculiar body forms or colors were designed for the one critical purpose of informing a prospective partner of desire and intent. By whatever means it was accomplished, the female responded and the next morning, after roosting next to each other all night without contest or argument, they mated. Their lives were joined and a new one of their very rare kind was promised to the world. A single egg would be laid, a miracle on its own account, and they would be triggered into yet another pattern that had remained locked up inside of them since they each began forming within the prison of their own eggs. These patterns were promised from the beginning and were fulfilled by coming to life at exactly the right time, not to further the ends of the individual birds involved but of the species, and of life as it is on this planet.

Chapter Fifteen

THE ENTIRE REPRODUCTIVE PROCESS through which the two birds had gone was the result of an incredibly complex chemical entering their bloodstreams. In each case, the source of the chemical was the pituitary gland. This minute gland, situated at the base of the brain, had masterminded the entire sequence in each bird. It had told the other glands when to go to work, had prompted the rapid and dramatic growth of reproductive organs within the birds, organs that at other times were small and insignificant, and would continue to direct the birds into their brooding stage, without which everything that had gone before would be meaningless. Unless the birds were prepared to care for the egg, and then their young, with meticulous concern and precision, their breeding would be a hollow sham.

In all, three distinctly different hormones would be discharged in the right sequence, at the right time, and in exactly the right quantities. From the point of view of species continuity the two condors were complex bundles of idle machinery. On signal from the small miracle glands they became functioning systems, hostages released from the bonds of their immaturity, turned on, productive, and legitimately heir to the history of life on earth.

Their mating took place in early March and it took the female only a matter of days to produce her single egg. At exactly the right moment, the fertilized and ripened ovum burst loose from the ovary and was moved down to the magnum of the oviduct by muscular contractions. There, in a matter of hours, a single undifferentiated layer of dense, jellylike albumen was applied. By the time the egg was formed and laid, the albumen would be broken down into layers, each contributing its own unique functions to the development and protection of the embryonic condor.

After receiving its albumen in the oviduct the ovum passed along to the isthmus, where two shell membranes were applied, moving from there to the uterus, where the shell and pigment were obtained. Some of the steps were accomplished in minutes, others took a day or more. By the time the egg reached the muscular vagina, it was a future condor, its food and its incubator. In its staggeringly complicated journey it traversed a system both perfect and beyond the duplicating powers of man. Even more than that, man could not even envision the system were there not birds to show us how it is done.

The chick that was to form within the sheltering envelope of the egg would be a male. The hormones the ovum had received from the female had so decreed. Just as the matter discharged by the pituitaries had set the whole system in motion, the even smaller quantities of sex-determining hormones would direct the development of the chick until it would hatch as the potential fatherer of others of its kind. A further miracle lay in the fact that throughout the species the ratio would be right. The percentage of males and females formed would give reasonable assurance of later matched pairs of condors duplicating the process, mankind not canceling it all with his violent disregard for the miracle of life.

During the period the egg components were forming and amalgamating within the female, the two condors remained close in everything they did. They perched side-by-side or one just above the other, they bathed together, and as a pair they soared beneath the clouds and above the canyons, scanning the broken land below for their required bounty of carrion. They selected a nest site and visited it often, although there was little for them to do. The site they chose was three thousand feet above sea level, seventy feet above a rough valley floor. It was twenty feet down from the top of a cliff and above it and below were steep slopes offering a virtual guarantee against intrusion by any but a winged species. A few feet in from the single entrance, near the sloping back wall, a dozen pebbles were pushed together in a random heap. Nothing more was done in way of preparation for another condor generation but it was enough, and even this had been dictated by glandular secretions working on a strict timetable within the pair.

At last the egg appeared, easily moved out of the vagina by smooth muscular ripples. Its appearance was proof that two more condors had received their full share of instincts and the due portion of the chemicals essential to their release and utilization. It was five inches long and was covered with tiny pits and excrescences. It was pale, barely greenish-blue in color, and weighed exactly ten and a half ounces. Its ovate ellipsoid shape contained two hundred and sixty cubic centimeters of material. There was room enough for the chick's growth and its sustenance. The system continued to be perfect.

At first the birds seemed puzzled by what they had done. They poked at the egg, rolling it around and stepping over it. Finally the female settled down on it, instinctively knowing that her warmth, and occasionally that of her mate, would be required for nearly a month and a half. It would be forty-two days before the egg would split apart, allowing a new condor to appear.

The adult condors took turns sitting on the egg. On occasion it was left unattended, but seldom did these naked periods exceed an hour. One or the other bird remained in the cave, guarding the egg against the night chill from three o'clock in the afternoon until the sun rose again in the eastern sky.

The egg lost weight steadily throughout the incubation period. Moisture evaporated through microscopic pores in the shell and, after the chick was formed and respiring, there were gaseous metabolic wastes. Nothing could be added once the egg was formed. The chick had to emerge from material already there.

On the fortieth day the birds became even more attentive than they had been since the egg first appeared. They inspected the egg every few minutes and both birds remained in the immediate vicinity of the nest. One or the other was on the egg at all times. There were small noises coming from within the shell and each time they occurred the parents became more excited. Once the male left the cave and returned holding the remains of a golden-mantled ground squirrel ready for regurgitating. He was prepared to feed the chick that had not yet been hatched. He was getting his signals in advance.

On the forty-first day the chick pipped his egg and punctured the shell, leaving a small dark hole near the blunter end. For a day and a night he hammered at his shell, driving the adults into a flurry of excitement. They did not offer to help him with the overwhelmingly difficult task but stood around, watching and listening, waiting for the chick to assert his right to survive. On the forty-second day a line began to form, radiating out from the original hole the chick had created. The line met on the far side of the egg after an hour and the end of the shell began to fall away. Inside, the baby condor collapsed in exhaustion and rested while light streamed into his dark cavity. After another hour he tumbled out of his egg altogether and lay on the cave floor, his small, greedy mouth ajar.

Both parents inspected their baby and nibbled at his sparse, wet, disorderly down. In some way, in some strange primitive way, they seemed to know that this was theirs and they felt for the helpless small bundle of ugly charm that which in a higher animal we might call love. It will probably forever remain a moot question whether or not a condor, or any *dumb* animal for that matter, actually *loves* its offspring. Semantics aside, and the dread anthropomorphism of the animal lover, the adult condors *acted* as if they did indeed love their baby and the result was the same.

Just as forces, chemical and physical, built up within the condors, creating by birth and destroying by age, so forces within the planet worked unseen, releasing unimaginably powerful energies to reduce, create, and alter their environment.

In a great, extravagantly looping arch, a seismic belt circles the Pacific Ocean. This ring accounts for eighty percent of the world's earthquakes. In California alone, thousands of shocks occur every year, and five hundred of these are strong enough to be felt by more than a few people. Fortunately, only one in ten thousand is severe enough to cause widespread or disastrously extensive local damage.

Earthquakes are tectonic in nature, they are caused by the very forces that gave California her mountains, much of her beauty, and the California condor its present home. Below the surface the crust is broken up into an endless series of enormous blocks separated by faults, long fracture lines that are veins of weakness in the masses of rock.

Over a period of time the blocks tend to shift, to move, to alter their position as gravity or heaven-only-knows-what forces play upon them. But there is friction, inertia, a tendency to hold against each other, a pushing inward toward the opposing member by weights that defy calculation. The two opposing forces of hold and give, of slip and stick, create strains the monumental size of which exceeds our imagination. The rock deforms, yields rather than slips, and the bending radiates back through the very structure of the minerals. But, inevitably, one day the strain is too much and something gives. The first movement is small, perhaps, but often bigger ones follow. Like coiled springs, the rocks let go, slide past each other horizontally, vertically, or both simultaneously and a wave of pain, a seismic shout of anguish, echoes throughout miles of solid rock and the land above shudders, for this is an earthquake.

There are thousands of fault lines in California. Many are celebrities, as so many criminals have been in history, and when their names are spoken there is often a slight hush in the voice of the speaker. Near Santa Barbara lies the Santa Ynez Fault. It is one small vein in a system so complicated it may never be fully defined. It is traceable by present means from Gaviota Pass east along the northern base of the Santa Ynez Mountains for a distance of sixty-five miles, which brings it perilously close to the area where the condors had nested. Just as it is itself part of a larger system, it has a system all of its own. Along its entire length smaller fault lines run in all directions where, in the deeper places, blocks snug against each other, gathering their strain and their anger.

It was past three o'clock in the afternoon and there had been no previous warning. A peregrine falcon had just stooped and gashed a mourning dove out of the sky. On opposite sides of the canyon two great-horned owls, unnaturally close to each other, perched and waited for the night.

The female condor was in the cave, preparing to settle down for the night with her downy chick, still too tender to face the night chill alone. Her fire was still needed. Ten miles distant her mate swung away from the path a golden eagle was carving across the sky. He was heading home, full of his bounty and ready to perch on an oak not far from the natal cave.

Amid the rubble on the canyon floor the buffy-gray form of a coyote played ghost with shadow and cover, seeking to end the life of a wood rat whose scent he had been following in its characteristic meandering course.

The foreshock was small, a ripple really, a slight nudge that puffed up a bit of dust here and shoved a pebble onto a rattling course there. But the two blocks beyond the hill and deep beneath the surface had had enough of each other. For centuries they had had the urge to move, to change their relationships, but they had been held by friction until their layers were bent and angry. The P wave, a sound wave, came undulating through the earth at a speed of three and a half miles a second. The earth along the line of its travel bounced slightly, heaved, and settled. Then, at two miles a second, the short S wave rolled and mingled with the slower but more lasting L or long wave.

At distant locations alarms sounded and seismologists rushed to their instruments, simple measuring devices that had been tied to the planet on firmly rooted and carefully situated concrete blocks. Teletypes rattled the recorded data and the men drifted back to their thoughts and their waiting games. The Richter Magnitude Scale had awarded the tremor a score of less than 4.0. No harm in that. Nothing to worry about or even to report beyond the routine daily records unless more warnings were signaled up to them through the planet's crust.

But in the canyon it had been something else. The rocky cliffs were old and in some places they were tired. Tens of thousands of shocks had assailed them before, some larger and some smaller than this, and rain and wind and just plain age had conspired to reduce their stability. The cliff itself, the eastern wall of the canyon, didn't change visibly in the grosser sense, but within it and on it and at its feet, where the shadows were deepest, some small changes did take place. The female condor, readying her chick and herself for the night, felt the shock and stood uncertainly, looking toward the opening of the cave, just beyond the reach of her beak. The second wave sent her forward to the edge of the shelf and the third motion that sallied upward within the cliff sent her tumbling off into space. Behind her the shallow, low cave closed like a mouth, as if the cliff had finished a yawn that was thousands of years old. When the male reached the canyon his mate would be gone, soaring away in despair and confusion and his chick would be a permanent part of the cliff. The alterations made by the quake were small, but they were large enough for this. The chick was dead and the year's crop of condors was poorer by one, by one-seventh of those that should have appeared to help the odds of survival. Nature has many things on her mind and was perhaps as concerned over her blocks of straining rock as she was over the condor species. By her actions she had denied the condor and his kind their due in his first year as a breeding adult. It is one of those things on which our philosophies cannot profitably reflect.

Chapter Sixteen

THE TWO CONDORS had been programmed by their pituitary glands to see their chick through to independence. By losing their object they entered into a period of confusion. The day after the earthquake had caused the cliff to swallow their chick they met near a water hole and began nibbling each other with almost savage intensity. The female, particularly, was lost in her frustration. She was alternately affectionate and hostile with her mate as she struggled blindly to divest herself of demands that she could no longer meet with purpose.

For several weeks after the tragedy both birds held food in their crops, as if about to feed their young, and flew about, seemingly looking for their nesting site. Then they would give up and sit hunched over on a perch, looking lost and abandoned, as indeed they had been, temporarily at least, by fate. On a number of occasions the male began displaying again and once the female seemed to be interested, but that, too, passed.

It is doubtful that either bird could remember the chick or understand even the vaguest outline of what had happened. Their lack of conscious knowledge was not the important thing, though, for that had come much later than they had in the animal scheme. Their real agony was in waiting for their instincts to dry up within them and release them from the now unneeded patterns into which they had been placed by their own chemistry.

Their constant nibbling of each other, the amount of energy they expended worrying feathers, pebbles and twigs that they found near bathing spots were displacement activities, as was the male's senseless sexual display and their occasional shows of bad temper.

There were days when they would soar together over dozens of miles of broken ground, flicking their shadows in and out of canyons, careening them against the walls of potholes, and sending them slithering up cliff faces to vanish at the brink before picking up again on the far-side downslope. They spiraled upward, at times reaching twelve thousand feet and more, there to hold briefly before beginning to drift slowly down, only to rise again. These were not games they were playing but aimless wandering, joyless travel through their time of trouble. At other times they would sit hunched over on perches for hours at a time, staring blindly down into the canyon below or facing into the scarred trunk of a long-dead tree. It was all hollow, all without immediate purpose, totally devoid of product or result.

But they had to remain alive, that drive was as strong within them as it had ever been, and in time the activities of life and living provided an outlet of sorts and that gave relief. It is not possible to say that these two darkly shrouded birds felt a sense of grief, not that perhaps, but they did feel something, and just as their tenderness and concern for their chick while it lived could be equated with our concept of love, so perhaps this was a parallel course with sorrow.

They often flew far for their food, hazardously far afield, for they flew into areas where the condor has not often been seen in nearly a century. Twice they were reported feeding beside a major highway far north of the preserves where they were relatively safe and where there were men who felt concern for their safety. Men who care about condors do not like to hear of their charges traveling far afield. It is hard enough to assure their safety where no guns are allowed and where man-travel can be successfully monitored.

In time their unfulfilled instincts crept away to hide in places where they would be safe for another time. The male chick that had been taken back into the land was a tragic loss for the species but he was not the treasure these two adult birds were. They were proven adults, birds that could and would reproduce themselves in kind.

Once while aloft they were mistaken for golden eagles and a small plane pursued them with a shotgun poking out of the cockpit door. Terrified by the steel-agony noise and the inexorable approach of the machine, they slipped away onto a different wind and found a canyon where the clumsy stiff-winged imitator could not follow.

Again when aloft, the male, temporarily alone, was assailed by two red-tailed hawks who made sport of his inoffensiveness, but beyond vomiting up his meal while almost a mile above the earth he suffered little, except in loss of dignity.

These were normal hazards in the life of a condor and they survived the winter and came again to spring. But it was an alternate year and they did not breed. Again they soared, ate, bathed, preened, and slept their way through a year of four seasons. Finally the time came again when the male could display with purpose and early in their third March together they bred for the second time. The process of the previous breeding year was repeated. The same inner swellings and awakenings enriched their bodies and gave them new purpose. The egg appeared and in forty-one days the chick broke free of his prison. Again it was a male and he had beaten his way out into the world in twenty-two hours less than their first chick. Their loss twenty-four months earlier was not a memory with them. Neither bird had any way of knowing whether or not they had successfully raised their first chick. They tackled the problem of protecting and providing for their new charge with the same fervor and with the same keen purpose. This time they were successful and eventually the chick was to travel with them as they flew their endless carrion-seeking course. Three dark birds now came to places where only two had come before. The parents still nibbled each other and their chick, even after he had grown to nearly their size.

The circular life course they now flew was as tight and gracefully purposeful as the circles they etched in the sky. Every other year they mated and, each time, they produced a single chick. The fifth egg they produced was sterile and they abandoned it after allowing it fifty-four days to hatch. Their frustration was almost as troublesome on this occasion as it had been when their first chick had been lost. But in their sixth breeding year together they again created a viable egg and resumed the contributory role to their species.

Their sixth egg was their last together, for shortly after their chick was able to fend for itself the female ran into mischance aloft. A low-flying monoplane made a familiar mistake — beyond the reach of game wardens and scientific patrol a shotgun spoke and, with the stunned and stupid look of death on her normally death-masked face, she fell to earth in a graceless, disjointed plunge. She bounced grotesquely when she hit, and lay like a broken shadow on the parched canyon floor. The plane circled once and when the white triangle on her left underwing became visible to the gunner for the first time, the plane grabbed furiously at the air, seeking altitude and anonymity. But the plane, too, had underwing markings and they were seen and recorded. The fine given by the court was light, only a token of society's disdain. However, the proven, producing female was dead, her potential permanently denied to the stream of condor survival. Actually, there was no punishment appropriate to the crime, not within a self-styled civilized society.

In his seventh breeding year the male condor mated with a female he had fathered in his third. It was her fourth chick. Her previous mate had inexplicably vanished from the census, his fate unknown to those who watched and wondered. His prematurely dead body lay rotting beneath a shroud of feathers, his leg securely held in a coyote trap that had been set and forgotten a dozen years earlier by an itinerant bounty hunter who had come and gone with the fortunes of whiskey.

The mating of the male with his own offspring may have been a mixed blessing for the species. A small group of birds already perilously inbred through the obvious arithmetic of their population was bred in even tighter. Slight and still invisible gene faults were accentuated, to what end no one can yet say. Their chick was needed but the species would have perhaps done better to gain a chick with new strains, new blood, new promise. This was an old promise repeated. But without another population to draw upon perhaps the event should not be despised. Imperfect although its ultimate potential may one day prove to be, and even that is hardly a certain thing, it was a chick and it did survive and it would one day prove to be fertile.

And so the seasons and the years of the male condor came to pass. Each alternate year he bred to his own offspring and produced a viable chick. He had survived a broken leg and captivity, a gunshot wound, pursuit by aircraft, poisoning — once by 1080 in his early years and twice by strychnine in his maturity.

He had found his rung on the ladder of condor society, and he had found all of his essential instincts in place and waiting when he had cause to call on them. Never once in his life was he conscious of self or even of life, yet he struggled valiantly to remain alive and to reproduce that self over and over again. He was driven, carried, thrust forward, and even gently moved by a species memory of how things were best done. He knew nothing consciously, yet knew everything in another way, everything that condors had known when North America belonged to camels and mastodons and saber-toothed cats. His blood knew what condors knew before there were men on earth and his genes knew everything the history of life on this planet could recall.

He had been an ugly creature all of his life. From the bulging-eyed, mangy-looking chick his own parents had so well treasured he had grown into a great gooselike bird with feathers dark enough to remind us that there were once witches in the consciences of men. The shadow he cast as he roamed the sky in the most magnificent of soaring flights flew scudding not only across broken ground but across shattered centuries and more. The noise his feathers made in flight were echoes of a thousand and a million years ago. The cleaning job he did on the land was an occupation essential now as it was essential then, before time had a meaning, before the concept of its passage was discernible. By the time he was twenty years old he had helped to rid the land of nearly eight thousand carcasses, and had personally consumed more than seven and a half tons of decaying animal flesh. That, too, was a contribution.

At twenty, the condor who had soared nearly a half a million miles over his mountainous range was tired. He had lived seven thousand and three hundred days, he had pressed himself to the bodies of two females, one of them his own offspring, and had produced a desperately needed crop of successful chicks. He was immortal. He had known peace, and he had known fear. He had cheated death more times than we can know and had thereby protected his potential, keeping it from harm until it was used up. His had been a successful life and he had lived it in the sun.

It was the breeding season again but the reproductive equipment within his body failed to swell. When he turned away from his daughter-mate and refused to display, she turned away from him and flew off across the canyon to where a recently matured bird was waiting. She could never think of the old bird, for that was clearly beyond her, and she would not recognize or acknowledge him when they met at bathing sites or on carcasses they found in common.

The old male spent more time on his perch now than he did aloft. There were days when he didn't bother to seek food but sat hunched down, his eyes half-closed and his beak slightly agape. He looked surprised, bewildered, as if he couldn't understand why he was being kept waiting.

On some days, when the sun was warm and the breeze exactly right, he seemed to revive, to soar again and to exert his position at the feeding ground. But those days became fewer and fewer. He was becoming forgetful and there were days when he didn't bathe. He became untidy and his feathers fell, leaving bald patches that were not only unsightly but interfered with the effectiveness of his complicated flight mechanism.

His decline was steady, a constant thing like everything else in his life had been. His cells were losing their memory, forgetting the things they knew when he and they were young. His brittle bones ached under the strain of movement and he limited himself as much as he could without actually starving. Younger birds were now pushing him off carcasses and he seldom ate his normal allotment of two pounds a day. He soared unsteadily over longer distances than were necessary, just to find a water hole that was not being used. Although he no longer bathed he did require water to drink and he preferred places where he would not be hissed away and insulted.

When he landed on a perch it was an unsteady maneuver and he no longer was willing to fly unless the wind was exactly right. He was ragged and sad and he had lived a little too long. And then, one morning, he was missing from his perch. No one noticed or cared, but where a condor had shrugged painfully into a sleeping posture at dusk there was a bare branch at dawn. The brush below the tree was thick and tangled and his body didn't show. But a coyote had her den site there and her cubs growled with mock anger as they tugged the carcass apart in their learning games. A single feather from his breast was left on exposed ground and as a soft eddy of wind began to move it around, a horned lark dropped down to collect it for her nest. In the nest she laid three olive-buff eggs sprinkled with drab and lavender, each of which would produce a bird far, far more beautiful than the condor had ever been.